# PREHISTORIC MAN

# PREHISTORIC MAN

\*

JOSEF AUGUSTA

Professor of Palaeontology

Illustrated under the direction of the Author

by

ZDENĚK BURIAN

Translated by Margaret Schierl

\*

629|

PAUL HAMLYN

London

Designed and produced by
ARTIA
for
PAUL HAMLYN
SPRING HOUSE • SPRING PLACE • LONDON NW5
© 1960 by Artia
*Printed in Czechoslovakia*
S 902

# CONTENTS

# INTRODUCTION

*Research into the historical development of plants and animals has produced a vast amount of irrefutable evidence that in ancient geological ages life was very different from that known today.*

*Our information does not take us back to the time when life first appeared on our planet, about one and a half thousand million years ago, but since then it has developed, and is constantly changing. It would thus be illogical to assume that the general law of evolution does not apply to man. From the biological aspect, it is impossible to conceive that man could have developed in any other way. Man owes his existence to a long line of ancestors; if one link in the chain were missing, man would not be what he is.*

*It has now been firmly established, on the basis of abundant evidence, that man developed from lower ancestors over many hundreds of thousands of years, and that, by origin, he is also a member of the animal kingdom.*

*The path of man's evolution was long and painful, strewn, not with roses, but with thorns and stones. It was, nevertheless, a journey worthy of admiration, since it led him out of the darkness of his early origins into the relative sunlight of the present day.*

*In this book we shall trace the route of man's journey. It will not be possible to pause at all the cross-roads, or to describe every detail of the itinerary. Sometimes we lose sight of the road, as if the sands of time had drifted across it; sometimes it can be seen clearly ahead, flooded with sunlight. That is why some parts of the way are still a subject of controversy, while elsewhere there is no longer any scientific doubt. One thing, however, is certain — man need not despise his lowly origin. On the contrary, he has every reason to be proud of his descent from ancestors who never accepted life as a gift, but who were obliged, from the outset, to win their existence by their own perseverance, ingenuity and labour.*

# MAN CONSIDERS HIMSELF

Since the dawn of history man has been interested in the mystery of his origin. At the same time, he naturally sought an answer to the question of the origin of the earth, the origin of water and of the firmament above.

In very ancient times, when man was still a primitive being, he answered these questions as best he could. He did not possess even the most elementary knowledge on which to base rational views, and relied either on his feelings and intuition, or let himself be carried away by imagination.

Even in those days there were two different explanations of the origin of man. One was based on the belief that man was created by God, or a number of gods. The other view, a primitive forerunner of the theory of evolution, held that man was developed from lower types of animals.

Primitive man did not regard himself as superior to other living creatures. Indeed, when he compared himself with certain animals, he was by no means offended at the idea of having originated from them, but wished he himself had comparable strength, agility and speed. That is why members of many primitive tribes still believe that their forefathers were descended from animals. Certain Red Indian tribes in California believe that they are descended from coyotes, that their ancestors walked on all fours and only later acquired human semblance, until by losing their tails and walking upright they eventually became human beings. The Iroquois Indians believe themselves to be descended from the mud terrapin, which was once plentiful in the swamps of their hunting grounds. Some Peruvian Indians believe that their original ancestor was the puma, which they accordingly worship. Certain East African natives look on the hyena as their ancestor, and dead hyenas are given a ceremonial burial. The Ainus, from the north of the Far East, believe themselves to be descended from dogs; and some of the natives of Borneo have an unusual explanation, claiming that the first man and woman came from a tree, made fruitful by a clinging vine.

There are many versions of man's origin by means of an act of creation, of which the Bible story is the best known. The Babylonian legend is similar, and much older; it held that man was fashioned from clay mingled with the blood of the god Bel. The ancient Egyptians also believed that a supreme god formed man from clay. The ancient Greeks believed that Zeus, king of the gods, formed man from clay, and that the kiss of the goddess Athene gave him life. Many natives living on the banks of the White Nile hold a similar belief; they are convinced that the different races were formed according to the clay used by the gods — white men from white clay and sand, the red and brown races from Egyptian clay, and the negroes from black earth deep in Africa.

The Polynesians have an interesting legend, to the effect that the first humans were formed by the gods from clay mixed with the blood of different animals. This is of deeper significance than the mere exchange of divine blood for animal blood, since these people believe that the first humans and their descendants were characterised by the features of the animals with whose blood the clay was mixed. If it was rat's blood they were thieves, if snake's blood they were false and treacherous, if cock's blood they were brave and persevering.

Some of the Greek philosophers, however, who were well acquainted with the beliefs of their own time and of earlier ages, were not satisfied with the explanations provided by religion, and attempted to find more natural, and hence more acceptable explanations.

Anaximander of Miletus (610—547 B.C.) and others assumed that animals had developed as a result of the action of the sun on water and mud, from which they believed the Earth had originally been formed, and that human beings had first existed in the guise of fish, which form they had lost only when thrown up on dry land.

Empedocles (496—430 B.C.) had a curious theory. He held that, at first, only plants were able to exist on Earth. Later, as a result of contact of the elements and the influence of love, individual parts of the body were formed, such as the head, legs, arms, eyes, etc.; these then joined together at random, often forming strange monsters, such as bulls with a human head and vice versa — in short, the monsters familiar from old myths and fairy-tales. These monsters, however, were not capable of living, and only creatures in which the parts truly belonged to one another survived. Empedocles declared that congenital malformations were reminders of these first monsters.

Anaxagoras (500—428 B.C.) also believed that men might have developed from fish or some other sea creatures. He was the first, however, to express the view that man owed his natural supremacy to his hands as well as to his intelligence. Anaxagoras did not believe in supernatural interference in nature by the gods and was therefore sentenced to death. His sentence was afterwards commuted to banishment for life.

While not expressing any individual view about the origin of man, Socrates (469—428 B.C.) considered that man's supremacy lay in his ability to fashion useful objects with his hands, and that it was to this unique gift that man owed his erect posture and bipedal manner of walking.

Aristotle (384—322 B.C.), the greatest of all the ancient naturalists, classified animals according to their degree of perfection. He did not separate man from the animal kingdom, but regarded him as part of it. He therefore termed man a *zoon*, the same name as he used for animals, but adding the word *politikon*, to emphasise that man was not the same as other animals. He also asserted that some animals were more closely related to man than others. Aristotle was persecuted for his materialist interpretation of natural development, and was finally obliged to flee from Athens to the island of Euboea, where he died.

Even in ancient times, some naturalists began to compare man with the anthropoid apes. The Carthaginian Hanno regarded the gorillas of the West African coast as hairy negroes, i.e. as human beings. The resemblance of the anthropoid apes to humans was so striking that they were given the name *homo silvestris* (forest man). In fact, the Malay word 'orang-utan' means 'man of the woods'.

From comparing man with the apes it was a small step to verifying their similarity by dissection. The history of anatomical research, however, was not simple. Only in ancient Egypt was the dissection of corpses permitted. In Aristotle's day a kind of academy was already established in Alexandria, which included a museum with a large collection of mummified animals. The oldest post-mortem reports in existence also came from Egypt. Egyptian medicine was highly developed, and doctors actually specialised in different branches of medicine. Reports showing that vivisection, the dissection of living human beings, was first carried out in Egypt, have also been preserved. One such doctor was Herophilus, and although he practised vivisection only on condemned criminals, he was nevertheless despised for doing such work. In ancient Rome the first autopsies were carried out by Galen of Pergamum (131—200 A.D.) on the corpses washed up on the banks of the Tiber.

Galen was the last great scholar of ancient natural and medical science. During the Dark Ages, science was unable to develop to any great extent, but later those gloomy years were illuminated by new scientific truths, boldly proclaimed by a few great men. Among them were Andrea Vesalius (1514—1564), author of the great classic *De corporis humani fabrica* (*The structure of the human body*); William Harvey (1578—1657), the anatomist, whose remarkable studies on the circulation of the blood laid the foundations of modern physiology; and Nicholas Tulp (1593—1674), whose studies on man and anthropoid apes were the beginning of comparative anatomy.

The question of the origin and development of man could not, however, be resolved simply by examining the structure of the human body and comparing it with the nearest mammals, particularly apes. It was necessary to resolve the problem of development in nature as a whole, and to determine what was due to chance and what was the outcome of definite laws. History itself made its own contribution. The development of overseas trade brought new information on other countries, and new knowledge of natural phenomena. More and more species of plants and animals were described, eventually necessitating some form of classification. After a number of attempts by other scientists, the famous Swedish naturalist Carl Linnaeus (1707—1778) finally evolved a system which forms the basis of the modern method of classification. Despite

12

its many original inaccuracies and deficiencies, which were later eradicated, Linnaeus's work was of immense fundamental importance, and is universally esteemed and valued.

It is, however, impossible to agree today with his view that plant and animal species are stable and immutable, and that they were thus created by God. 'Tot sunt species, quot ab initio creavit infinitum Ens' ('There are as many species as were created in the beginning by the Infinite Being') is a well-known sentence which he wrote in his *Classes plantarum* (*Plant classes*) in 1738. It is only fair to mention, however, that towards the end of his life Linnaeus no longer believed implicitly in his own words, since he observed that new species were still capable of being formed.

Although Linnaeus was a good Christian, and firmly believed in the Bible version of the creation, he nevertheless classified man and the anthropoid apes in a single category, separately from other Primates. Thus, Linnaeus, probably without meaning to do so, actually labelled man as the highest of the mammals.

During the first half of the eighteenth century, increasing numbers of discoveries brought to light new facts which could not be explained from the creationist point of view. Naturalists saw with increasing clarity that species are not immutable, as was generally believed and taught. One of the first to oppose creationism was Michail Vassilyev Lomonosov (1711—1765) who declared that fossils were not freaks of nature, but the remains of living organisms which were the ancestors of contemporary living creatures. Afanasy Kaverznyev (1742—c. 1820) published a book on the transformation of animals, pointing out that one species develops from another, and that all are more or less related. Karl Franzevich Rulye (1814—1856), professor of Moscow University, also taught that natural phenomena are inter-related and inter-dependent, stressing the inseparability of organisms and their environment, and ascribing changes in organisms mainly to environmental factors. Rulye also studied fossils and demonstrated that the Earth was once uninhabited, that its first inhabitants were marine plants and animals, followed by amphibian and terrestrial forms, and that man was included in this progression.

The idea of an association between animal and plant life, of the development of animals and plants from lower to higher forms, and of a relationship between man and animals was also gaining ground in France, though there were two distinct schools of thought in connection with this last relationship. The first, which was characteristic of French materialist philosophers, refused to recognise the existence of a qualitative difference between man and animals, whilst the second, finding expression chiefly in the works of the naturalist Georges Louis Buffon (1707—1788), stressed the sharp contrast between them in the intellectual sphere, while admitting the similarities of their physical structure.

Buffon was well acquainted with the work of anatomists, and himself had the opportunity to examine the structure and habits of the gibbon. He assumed, however, that the soul was manifested only in the form of thought, and that only man possessed a soul. Animals, as distinct from man, do not govern their weaker fellows but devour them; they do not speak, or develop their capabilities. There seemed to Buffon to be a deep gulf between man and animals, incapable of being bridged because of the mental differences which precluded the possibility of man evolving from lower orders. Buffon was the first Frenchman to claim that in earlier geological ages the Earth was inhabited by fauna and flora since, to a large extent, vanished; and that the development of new species was due not only to environmental conditions but also to breeding by man. He was convinced that both animals and plants sprang from a few primitive groups.

Buffon did not, however, have the courage of his convictions. When called to task by the theological faculty of the Sorbonne, and asked to explain why his views differed from the teachings of the Bible, he hastened to proclaim that the biblical version was the true one and that his own opinions were mere hypotheses.

Buffon's claim that a fundamental difference existed between the mental abilities of men and animals, though correct, impeded his further progress, whereas the French materialist philosophers recognised no such dividing line. Yet on neither side were the errors profound enough to prevent their ideas forming a basis for more modern and advanced views on the subject. Even at that time the first voices were being raised explaining the development of vegetable and animal species on a natural basis. Chief among them

13

was the famous philosopher Jean Baptiste Lamarck (1744—1829), who in his classic *Philosophie zoologique* (1809) declared that progressive development could be observed in the animal realm, that higher animals sprang from lower species, and that man was descended from man-like apes. He rejected the creationist theory and attempted to demonstrate the influence of environment on the variation between the species. An important part in this process was, in Lamarck's view, played by some fluid circulating in the body and sending impulses to those parts of the body in which variations were made necessary by changes in the environment.

These views cannot, however, detract from the importance of Lamarck's work. His theories were remarkable for his day, being based on the conception of the historical development of the entire organic world. He was the first to elaborate a complete theory of the evolution of living organisms, and the first to express clearly the idea that developing organisms were directly influenced by environment, and that changes were related to the way in which their organs were used under given biological conditions.

His chief error was to fail to support his brilliant conjecture by sufficiently weighty evidence and proof. His opponents pounced on this fact, alleging that his whole theory was false, and did their utmost to doom him to oblivion. This is best demonstrated by the words engraved on his monument in the Jardin des Plantes, where he worked for many years. The monument shows Lamarck's daughter reading to her aged, blind father, and beneath are the words, *La postérité vous vengera, mon père!* ('Posterity will avenge you, father!'). These words, indeed, came true. Judged on the sound core of his teaching, Lamarck may rightly be regarded as the father of evolutionary theory, in its broadest sense.

Lamarck found a comrade-in-arms in another French naturalist, Etienne Geoffroy de Saint-Hilaire (1772—1844), the founder of the zoological gardens in Paris. Saint-Hilaire arrived at the same conclusions as Lamarck, but by a different route. From his studies on comparative anatomy and embryology he was convinced that all animals are formed according to a basic form or type. He regarded environmental influences as the main cause of deviations from type. He was also interested in fossils, and stated that they must have been the forerunners of modern animals, differing in this respect from Lamarck, who repudiated the idea of extinction of species and took the view that all fossil types still existed, although their offspring had altered to a lesser or greater degree.

One of the many opponents of these new and disturbing ideas was Georges Cuvier (1769—1832), an outstanding French scientist and founder of modern palaeontology; it was he who laid the foundations of palaeontological research on the basis of morphology and comparative anatomy. In his studies of mammalian fossils he recognised that mammals of different types lived in different geological ages; but being a confirmed follower of Linnaeus as regards immutability of species, he asserted that catastrophes occurred at times, destroying all life, and that afterwards life had to be created anew. Cuvier therefore did not accept Lamarck's teachings, and at Lamarck's memorial ceremony merely remarked, *en passant*, that they were not sufficiently substantiated to be acceptable. A clash of opinions occurred between Cuvier and Saint-Hilaire, from which Cuvier, the recognised authority, not unnaturally emerged victorious. Cuvier was, nevertheless, a great scientist, whose remarkable life's work greatly contributed to the advance of palaeontological research in other directions.

Cuvier's opposition to evolutionary ideas had a detrimental influence on natural scientific trends of the time, and it appeared likely that these ideas might be buried indefinitely. No mere authority, however, was able to silence them completely. It was, nevertheless, more than half a century—counting the years from Lamarck's first publication of his theories — before Charles Darwin (1809—1882) revived the theory of evolution, and won recognition for it after a hard fight with other naturalists of the day.

Darwin, one of the most celebrated naturalists in history, studied for many years material which he collected in a five years' voyage round the world in the ship *H. M. S. Beagle*, and came to the conclusion that species are not stable and immutable, that present-day plants and animals are not the same as the species which existed in the earliest times, but that they are descended from them and hence linked to them by evolution.

Darwin's theories will not be discussed in detail here, as they are now generally known. It should be emphasised, however, that since they were backed by a wealth of irrefutable evidence, they marked an important turning-point in the development of the natural sciences. Darwin's theory of evolution, some points of which have since been corrected or supplemented, sounded the death-knell for all other theories claiming that nature does not change and is not based on an historical process.

It was obviously impossible to omit man from such a theory; even Lamarck had not forgotten him, for he said, 'If some strain of particularly highly developed apes were compelled by the conditions of existence, or by some other cause, to relinquish their arboreal habits and were obliged, for many generations, to use only their legs for walking, there is no doubt that such quadrupeds would ultimately become bipeds, and that their toes would lose the property of opposition, i.e. of placing the great toe against the others. If these creatures made an effort to stand upright, so as to scan and dominate their surroundings, there is no doubt that their legs would become adapted to an erect posture and that they would have difficulty in walking on all fours. If such animals did not use their jaws as weapons, for biting, rending and gripping, but only for chewing, the jaw would decrease in size and would gradually acquire human semblance.' Lamarck went on to describe how such creatures would inevitably dominate all other creatures, not only because of the changes in their physical structure, but also because of their mental capacities.

It is interesting to note that in his *Origin of Species* Darwin did not discuss the origin of man. The omission was intentional, since in a letter to a scientist friend he admitted that he had purposely avoided the question of the development of man from apes, by reason of the prejudices with which this problem was surrounded. He soon realised, however, that silence was impossible. In the conclusion to his book he remarked that the origin and evolution of plants and animals must also throw light on the question of the origin and development of man. He also was fiercely attacked by the fanatical opponents of the evolutionary theory, who objected to man — created in the image of God — being 'lowered' to the level of animals.

Darwin did the best thing possible, both for himself and his cause. He ignored the vituperation and began to collect scientific material on the problem of man's natural progression. When his evidence was complete, he wrote *The Descent of Man*, published in 1871. This book, which rounded off his work, clearly and convincingly demonstrated that evolution also applied to man, and that man, far from holding a special place in nature, was only the last and highest link in the chain of development of life as a whole. He produced abundant evidence on man's relationship with other animals, particularly apes, and showed that man and the anthropoid apes had common ancestors who lived in bygone geological ages.

Darwin went still further. Not being satisfied merely to determine that man's ancestors could be found among Quaternary or Tertiary apes, he endeavoured to explain the course of their development, especially in the early stages. He drew attention to the significance of bipedal locomotion and of freedom of the hands, pointing out that for many operations it was essential for both hands and the upper part of the trunk to be free, so that man must therefore stand firmly on his feet. Elsewhere he wrote that man could not have attained his present supremacy without his hands, which are so admirably adapted to work in accordance with his will. He stressed, furthermore, that man, even at the most primitive stage of development, was still the mightiest creature ever to appear on the Earth, chiefly because of his powers of reason and gregarious habits; and he attempted to discover the conditions which resulted in man and his ancestors acquiring the ability to construct tools, expressing the view that men progressed from breaking stones at random to fashioning them into explicit forms.

The conception that man developed from animal ancestors is now supported by many discoveries of bones of prehistoric anthropoid apes, ape-men and prehistoric human beings, and is now generally acknowledged as fact. There is still disagreement on many points, but doubtless these details will ultimately be resolved.

# PREHISTORIC MAN APPEARS

# ON THE SCENE

When Darwin published his *Origin of Species* in 1859, he caused a tremendous stir among the still waters of old concepts and theories. His book aroused amazement and disdain, admiration and hatred. Only a few immediately recognised its importance, and realised that it formed the basis of a new approach to the main problems of biological science. Among the first supporters and protagonists of the new theories were two great scientists, Thomas Huxley of Britain and Ernst Haeckel of Germany.

## THE JAVA MAN (PITHECANTHROPUS)

In his book *Natürliche Schöpfungsgeschichte* ('History of Natural Creation'), published in Berlin in 1868, Haeckel expressed the bold idea that from the evolutionary aspect it was essential that there should be a transitional link between the apes and man, possessing characteristics of both. This later became famous under the name of the 'missing link'. Haeckel termed the link 'Pithecanthropus', a name composed of the Greek words *pithecos* (ape) and *anthropos* (man).

To many scientists, Haeckel's postulate appeared to have insufficient foundation, to others it seemed simply fantastic. One man, however, who was inspired by Haeckel's conception of Pithecanthropus was Eugène Dubois, assistant to the famous anatomist Max Fürbringer and lecturer in anatomy at Amsterdam University. He was determined to make the effort to discover the 'missing link' and thus not only to confirm Haeckel's theory but also to provide significant support for Darwin's teachings.

Dubois' investigations led him to the conclusion that the bones of Pithecanthropus might be found in the East Indies, but in view of the distance involved and the fact that he was not a wealthy man this raised immediate difficulties. He could arouse no official support for his scheme, and decided to leave the university to enter the Dutch colonial army as a doctor. At the end of October, 1887, he sailed for Sumatra, where he started work in the hospital at Pandong.

As soon as he had settled down he spent all his free time making extensive excavations, all of which he paid for out of his own pocket. He explored a whole series of caves near Pandong, but without result. Three years passed, and still there was no sign of Pithecanthropus.

Fortunately Dubois persevered, despite repeated failures and financial strain. In 1889 he came into possession of fragments of a skull found near the village of Wadjak in Java. After placing the fragments together, Dubois found that it was an australoid type of skull, unlike that of the natives of Java. As a result, he applied for transfer to Java, and in 1891 and 1892 his excavations there were crowned with success. On the banks of the river Solo, near Trinil, he found first a molar, then the top of a skull with highly developed supraorbital ridges, followed by the discovery of a complete thigh-bone, and finally of another molar. These bony parts were all scattered, but were found in the same layer, not far from one another. Dubois was convinced that they were all parts of the same individual, whom he supposed to have been the victim of a volcanic eruption, together with the large and small animals whose bones also lay in the Trinil volcanic tufa. The bones had evidently been caught up later in the bed of the Solo and carried away by the water; nothing was known of the other parts of the skeleton, nor whether they would ever be found.

In 1894 Dubois published a detailed account of his finds in German, under the title, *Pithecanthropus erectus, eine menschenähnliche Übergangsform aus Java* ('*Pithecanthropus erectus*, a man-like transitional form from

Java'). Dubois believed that he had actually found a creature whose bones showed it to be a higher form than the anthropoid apes, but lower than man — in other words a creature which fitted Haeckel's description of the 'missing link'. He therefore named this creature *Pithecanthropus*, adding the term *erectus*, since the form of the thigh-bone clearly indicated that it had walked upright.

While the initial excitement in scientific circles still raged around his discovery, Dubois proceeded with further excavations in Trinil. When they bore no result, he returned, in 1895, to Holland. By this time his Pithecanthropus was famous, and the subject of animated discussion in the scientific world. Now, however, new doubts and problems were raised. There were three basic questions — whether the bones really belonged to the same individual, what was the geological age of the stratum in which they were found (Dubois considered it to be of the Pliocene age, i.e. of the latest division of Tertiary formations), and whether Pithecanthropus was an ape, a man or a transitional link. The first question was perforce left open, the second was answered by studying the bones of animals collected by a special expedition sent to Trinil for this purpose in 1907. Abundant mammalian bone material showed that the stratum in which Dubois had found his bones belonged to the middle of the early Quaternary (Pleistocene). The third question could not be answered satisfactorily, because the material was insufficient; more complete remains were needed.

The excavations in Trinil naturally aroused great interest among the natives, who began collecting bones and teeth washed up by the river Solo in flood. Many visitors also came to Trinil in the hope of obtaining scarce and valuable relics. Eventually, new specimens were found on Java. An important part in their discovery and identification was played by G.H.R. von Koenigswald, now professor of historical geology and palaeontology at Utrecht University in Holland. He came to Java in 1927, as a palaeontologist in the service of the Dutch, who at that time were carrying out new geological research on Java.

The skull of the next Pithecanthropus was discovered near the village of Modjokerto, in an important oil-bearing area. The skull was small and at first glance closely resembled that of a human child. The cranial cavity was, however, obviously too small, and since the skull was found in a stratum of considerable geological age, it was correctly deduced that it was that of some Pithecanthropus. When the name *Pithecanthropus modjokertensis* was suggested, however, Dubois, now professor of mineralogy, geology and palaeontology at Amsterdam University, protested sharply. He asserted that his specimen was not a human being and that this skull of human appearance could not be so described. In concession to Dubois, therefore, the skull was termed *Homo modjokertensis*.

One difficulty in identifying this skull was that it was found in older (Lower Pleistocene) layers, known as Djetis Beds, whereas the original *Pithecanthropus erectus* was discovered in more recent (Middle Pleistocene) Trinil Beds. The problem was settled by von Koenigswald's finds of the remains of *Pithecanthropus* in Sangiran, again in Lower Pleistocene Djetis strata. A fragment of lower jaw, complete with teeth, and a skull, intact except for the facial part and upper jaw, demonstrated without a doubt that *Pithecanthropus* was the most primitive type of human being. This was further confirmed by later finds.

The Sangiran specimens were also described as *Pithecanthropus modjokertensis*, and although geologically older, were pronounced to be a somewhat lower type than the classic *Pithecanthropus erectus*. This is seen from the presence of a small space (diastema) — common in anthropoid apes — about 4 mm. wide between the upper incisors and the canines, although the latter are not particularly large, suggesting that the point of the lower canine stood above the crowns of the other teeth. The cranial capacity is also small — only 800 c.c.

All these investigations proved that the Java Pithecanthropus lived at the time of the Lower and Middle Pleistocene — about 500,000 to 300,000 years ago.


## THE SINANTHROPUS OF CHINA

Remains of man's forebears (Prehominids) were not, however, confined to Java. Large cave sites were found relatively recently near Choukoutien, in China. These discoveries were of tremendous value.

Choukoutien is about thirty miles south-west of Peking, and is surrounded by hills of Silurian limestone, with numberless fissures and caves. The Swedish geologist, J. G. Andersson, drew the attention of the Swedish palaeontologist, O. Zdansky, to Choukoutien, where the latter collected the bones of fossil mammals. On sorting these he found two teeth of human type, which he cautiously termed *Homo* sp., i.e. the teeth of some species of true human being. The report of the Choukoutien teeth was circulated only among a small circle of experts, and great interest was shown by Davidson Black, then Professor at the Medical College in Peking. He examined the teeth and confirmed Zdansky's view that they were of human origin, but that they belonged to an older geological period.

Professor Black, anxious to obtain further material, immediately started excavations in Choukoutien, which lasted from the spring to the autumn of 1927, without any result. Just before work stopped, however, a lower molar was found, its most striking feature being the low crown and large pulp-cavity. Black called it the 'most important tooth in the world,' and on the basis of his find, established a new genus and species, which he called *Sinanthropus pekinensis*. Though most of the experts felt that Black had reached too far-reaching conclusions from the evidence of a single tooth, subsequent discoveries completely vindicated him.

On Black's untimely death, excavations at Choukoutien continued under the directorship of Dr Franz Weidenreich, and lasted until the Japanese invasion in 1937. Weidenreich subsequently went to the United States where he published a comprehensive summary of the Choukoutien discoveries. In these he had been assisted by W. C. Pei, now Professor at Peking University. In 1928, two fragments of lower jaws were found, one belonging to an adult, the other to a child about eight years old. The most important discovery, however, was in December 1929, when a perfectly preserved skull cap was excavated. Between 1927 and 1937, skeletal remains of about forty individuals were found near Choukoutien, including over one hundred teeth, fragments of six skulls and fragments of limb bones and other bones.

This priceless material was unfortunately lost during the Second World War. Excavations were resumed in 1949 by the Chinese Academy of Sciences. Since previous finds were so abundant, and the area has by no means been fully investigated, it is to be hoped that the new diggings and potential finds will make good the losses caused by the war.

The skeletal remains of the Choukoutien *Sinanthropus* were found together with the bones of characteristic warmth-loving animals, showing that he lived during the first (Günz-Mindel) Interglacial Period, or at the beginning of the second (Mindel-Riss).

From the point of view of form and structure, *Sinanthropus* is very similar to *Pithecanthropus*, and some experts term it *Pithecanthropus pekinensis*. *Sinanthropus* also has large, thick supraorbital ridges, thick skull bones, a markedly receding forehead, and other features of a primitive character. The capacity of the cranial cavity of the largest individuals is over 1,000 c.c. The fact that the bones were broken into fragments is regarded by many as a sign of cannibalism, though Professor Pei declares this to be incorrect.

The contemporary fauna of *Sinanthropus* has been studied since the War in detail by Professor C. Yang, and by Père P. Teilhard de Chardin. Apparently it included prehistoric elephants, rhinoceroses, wild horses, gazelles, deer, wild pigs, bears, wolves, foxes, porcupines, hedgehogs, frogs, ostriches and a variety of rodents.

One very important fact established about *Sinanthropus* was that he knew fire. Large hearths were found in the caves which served him as a dwelling, and the fire, which was doubtless obtained accidentally from forest or steppe fires, was kept alight with the wood of a species of Judas tree (*Cercis blackii*). It was not only a source of warmth in the cold, damp caves and a means of protection against wild animals, but also used for roasting meat, as evidenced by the finding of numerous burnt bones.

Large numbers of stone implements, mainly fashioned from quartz, were also found in Choukoutien. The commonest implements were scrapers and various pointed tools. Bowls made from antelope skulls were also discovered. The horns were broken off, and together with the crown of the skull, formed a kind of tripod upon which the bowl rested.

# OTHER PRECURSORS OF MAN

Bones of man's forebears were not found only in Java and China. In Europe, remains were found in Germany. In 1907, a complete, well-preserved lower jaw was found in a sand-pit near the village of Mauer, near Heidelberg. This jaw, which is officially known as the Mauer or Heidelberg jaw, was discovered in undisturbed layers at a depth of 24 metres (87 feet). It was sent to Professor Schoetensack of Heidelberg University, who published a detailed description in 1908. The being to which the jaw belonged was named *Homo heidelbergensis*, but since it was not unanimously regarded as the jaw of a human being, other generic names were suggested. The evidence is insufficient to be decisive, since no more of the skull is known.

Further remains were found in Africa, including about two hundred small fragments from the skulls of three or four individuals, by Kohl-Larsen in the region of Lake Eyassi or Nyarasa. Professor Weinert, who did much research on *Sinanthropus*, pieced together one skull from these fragments, which in some respects resembles that of *Sinanthropus*. The skull, which was given the designation *Africanthropus njarasensis*, belongs to the late Pleistocene period. It should be mentioned, however, that some authorities disagree with Weinert's reconstruction, and regard the fragments either as those of a Neanderthaloid or of *Homo sapiens*.

In 1954, C. Arambourg and R. Hoffstetter found two jaw-bones in an old sand-pit at Ternifint, near the village of Palikao, south-east of Mascara in Algeria. One — of a robust character and probably that of a male — was almost intact, while of the other — slighter and probably that of a female — only the left half was preserved. In some respects these jaws were similar to those of *Pithecanthropus* or *Sinanthropus*, but since they were not identical with either, the beings from which they came were called *Atlanthropus mauritanicus*. The layer in which these finds were made also contained the bones of hippopotami, elephants, rhinoceroses, zebras, giraffes, camels, and different species of antelopes and beasts of prey. Some of these go to show that geologically these strata belong to the beginning of the Middle Pleistocene.

This second African find was also interesting because it showed that this individual was probably a user of the Chelles-Acheul hand-axe industry. More than one hundred stone implements fashioned from quartzite, flint or limestone were found, all rough and primitively sharpened to a point. This stone industry, known throughout the warmer parts of the Old World, is likewise placed by prehistorians at the beginning of the Middle Pleistocene.

It should be clear, therefore, that the geographical distribution of man's precursors was quite considerable. It is to be hoped that further discoveries will make the picture of geographical distribution and density of population even clearer than at present.

According to some experts, Prehominids such as *Pithecanthropus*, *Sinanthropus*, *Protanthropus* (Germany), *Africanthropus* and *Atlanthropus*, form a special sub-family which they call Archanthropinae. All are believed to have lived 500,000 to 300,000 years ago. They represent a very important and significant stage in man's early development, and already show a great advance on their animal ancestors. In subsequent ages man developed independently into a being endowed with reason and a highly elaborate nervous system. His social life became progressively more complex; his speech became ever more articulate; his implements assumed more ingenious and intricate forms. The stage of the Prehominids is thus the beginning of man's development proper, the point at which he parts company with the animals.

# MAN'S ANIMAL ANCESTORS

The discovery of the Javan *Pithecanthropus* provided convincing evidence that the theory of man's development from lower animal forms was correct. In addition to strictly human features, the bony remains of *Pithecanthropus* also displayed some features of anthropoid apes, and this was confirmed by subsequent discoveries of other Prehominids.

Although there is, therefore, no doubt of man's descent from the lower Primates, via the higher anthropoid apes and thence to the most primitive human types, it must be stressed that man is not descended from the anthropoid apes extant today. These are a parallel branch, developing alongside the human branch, though probably from a common ancestor.

## THE ORIGIN OF MAN'S ANIMAL ANCESTOR

Man's animal forerunner can be sought only among the primaeval apes, whose evolution was long and complicated. The only branches considered in this book are those with a significant bearing on the origin of man.

Between sixty and fifty million years ago, at the beginning of the Tertiary, semi-apes developed from insectivora. They soon divided into two branches, one of which produced the broad-nosed monkeys of the New World *(Platyrrhina)* and the other the narrow-nosed monkeys of the Old World *(Catarrhina)*, anthropoid apes and man. For the present subject, the former branch is of no significance and only the second will be considered.

The oldest remains of a monkey-like animal were found in Lower Tertiary (Eocene) strata in Burma. They consist of a fragment of a lower jaw, and are described by the name *Amphipithecus*. Much more important were the finds made in the Fayyum, south of Cairo, in Egypt. The most interesting is *Parapithecus*, which was the starting-point of the branch leading to the narrow-nosed monkeys of the Old World. The lower jaw of *Parapithecus* was found in the Lower Oligocene, together with *Propliopithecus*. The latter appears to have been the precursor of *Pliopithecus*, known from German finds. *Pliopithecus* was probably the precursor of the present-day gibbons. The most important genus of all, however, is *Dryopithecus*, which lived at the end of the Tertiary, during the Miocene and Pliocene periods. *Dryopithecus* was a widely distributed genus and its remains have been found in Germany, Austria, Czechoslovakia, France, Spain, Egypt, India and China.

The *Dryopithecus* group is marked by a particular primitive pattern of the enamel-cusps of the lower molars. This is shared to some extent by the living anthropoids and even to a lesser extent by man, suggesting that in the ancestry of both ape and man we must include a *Dryopithecus*-like stage.

*Dryopithecus* is not the only fossil anthropoid ape known; other forms include *Sivapithecus* (Indian Miocene), *Udabnopithecus* (East Georgia, U. S. S. R.), and others, but none is as important as *Dryopithecus*. Two comparatively recent finds, however, while not themselves immediate forerunners of man, nevertheless show that the early stages of man's evolution are more complicated than they once seemed. One of these was the discovery of an anthropoid ape, named Proconsul, found in 1933 and 1948 in Middle Miocene strata in Kenya, near Lake Victoria; the other was the finding of *Oreopithecus*, whose entire skeleton was discovered in September 1958, in Pliocene lignite in Tuscany, Italy.

Although more than twenty different species of fossil anthropoid apes are now known, it still appears that the branch which led to man originated among the Dryopithecinae, or similar, closely related types. None of the present-day apes, therefore, is an ancestor of man.

## HUMANIZATION OF THE APES

How can we trace the path of man's evolution? From the viewpoint of form and structure, it consists chiefly in the raising of the body to an erect position, in an increase in the size of the brain and in its differentiation, in refinement of the features, and in the development of the limbs into hands and feet. Simultaneously, instinctive actions were transformed into conscious ones, and finally gave rise to abstract thought.

Of course, these changes were extremely complex and gradual. About the middle of the Tertiary, towards the end of the Miocene or beginning of the Pliocene period, some of the anthropoid apes of the time — possibly *Dryopithecus* — split roughly into two branches. The descendants of the one branch remained in the primaeval forest, whilst those of the other ventured first to the edge of the forests and later into the steppes, where there were only few trees. During the Late Tertiary the climate turned colder, already heralding in the Quaternary Ice Age, and it is possible that cooling or drought greatly reduced the primaeval forests.

The environmental change from forest to steppe, where the grass was interspersed with small copses and isolated trees, altered the lives of these anthropoid apes. Their ancestors, and their relatives who remained in the forest, lived on berries, young shoots, roots and bulbs, insects, worms, birds' eggs and young mammals. They made their homes mainly in the trees, where they sheltered from beasts of prey. The apes of the steppe were obliged to alter their manner of living in order to survive, and this they did by relinquishing their climbing habits and four-footed walk, for a two-legged walk and a complete alteration of diet. Although some differentiation of the fore and hind limbs had already occurred in the anthropoid apes as compared with lower animals, the fore limbs were still used for swinging and climbing. On the ground these animals walked only short distances on their hind limbs, and even then with an unsteady gait. The anthropoid apes of the steppe, however, perfected this capacity.

This change in the manner of locomotion resulted in the acquisition of an erect posture, closely associated with certain changes in bodily structure. The long arms grew shorter, the shoulders broader. The relatively short legs increased in length, and the flat feet were gradually replaced by a flexible arched foot which absorbed the shock involved in walking. The form and position of the heel also changed. The great toe thickened and ranged itself beside the other toes. The action of walking also required different muscular formations, and the calf of the leg made its first appearance.

Erect walking also resulted in a change in the body's centre of gravity. The firm support of the body, the spine, acquired new curvatures. Changes occurred in the arrangement of the viscera and in the structure of the pelvis, which acquired a shallow, bowl-shaped form. The head, which in the anthropoid apes was bent, was gradually raised. The facial expression altered, and the size of the cranium increased. The foramen magnum shifted forward in the base of the skull. The powerful teeth, with their large canines, grew smaller as they lost the function of tearing and rending.

The liberation of the hand from walking left it free for defence against enemies, for seizing sticks and killing animals, for digging larvae and tasty roots out of the ground. Fragments of stone could be broken and points and edges used for specific purposes. These were the first artificially produced implements, though simple and primitive. From here, however, it was only a short step to chipping the stones for sharpening, or forming the ends of sticks into points.

Changes in diet also played an important role. The deficiency of plant food, with which the forest abounded, had to be made good by meat, and this had to be obtained by hunting. Since the anthropoid apes of the steppe were not as physically adapted as their forest brothers, they had to learn to hunt together in groups, armed with sticks, stones, fragments of bone or sharp horns. Instinctive behaviour gradually changed to voluntary action.

All these changes had to take place before purely simian forms — possibly some of the Dryopithecinae — could develop into the forebears of the most primitive human beings. The process lasted for hundreds of thousands of years. In man's general evolutionary history, it is the first and basic stage, the era of man's animal precursor, while the latter was still a member of the animal kingdom and still subject to the general laws of evolution.

# THE AUSTRALOPITHECINAE

# OF SOUTH AFRICA

It has already been stated that in the Later Tertiary, chiefly during the Miocene, there were many non-specialised types of anthropoid apes distributed over wide areas of Europe, Asia and Africa. At that time they were the highest evolutionary types, and some eventually developed into man. Among the initial forms in this process we find the South African *Australopithecinae*, which, while probably not themselves the direct ancestors of the earliest and most primitive human beings, nevertheless give us a good idea of what they must have been like.

In 1924, Raymond Dart, Professor of Anatomy at the University of the Witwatersrand, Johannesburg, was given a skull, found in a limestone quarry near Taungs, in Bechuanaland. The skull was found to consist of a natural cast in limestone of the cranial cavity, an almost complete facial part, the upper and lower jaw, together with the teeth, and the right side of the skull. The teeth showed it to be about six years old. Dart immediately identified it as the skull of an anthropoid ape, but was surprised to find that it also displayed many human as well as simian features. The position of the foramen magnum at the base of the skull showed that the balance of the skull was similar to that of a human being, indicating a more erect posture than is usual in anthropoid apes. From certain features of the cranial cavity Dart deduced that higher cerebral function enabled this creature to live in an environment different from that in which anthropoid apes had lived previously, and in which they live today.

The ecological conditions of the area in which the skull was found showed that this anthropoid ape was no longer a strictly forest-dwelling type, but that it lived among rocks and cliffs overlooking woodless plains covered with grass, bushes and occasional trees. It had thus become a dweller of the steppes, living in groups of varying sizes among the rocks, and seeking shelter from the elements and from enemies in caves and fissures. It was obliged to alter its diet and lived predominantly on meat. The remains of the fauna found with its bones showed that its food consisted mainly of baboons and antelopes.

Professor Dart naturally attached great importance to this find, and in February 1925 submitted a preliminary report in which he named the creature to which the skull belonged *Australopithecus africanus* (literally 'African southern ape') and stated that it was much closer to man than any other fossil anthropoid ape, and represented an evolutionary stage between the anthropoid apes and man.

The response of the experts was lukewarm. They were sceptical about Dart's view that *Australopithecus* was probably Haeckel's famous but undiscovered Missing Link. The prevalent opinion was that the Taungs find was nothing more than a variety of chimpanzee.

Two scientists, however, supported Dart's theory. One was Aleš Hrdlička, an American of Czech origin and director of the anthropology department of the National Museum in Washington, and the other was Dr Robert Broom, a prominent British palaeontologist, famous for his explanation of the development of mammals and reptiles, and later a member of the Transvaal Museum in Pretoria. Broom immediately recognised the importance of the skull of *Australopithecus* for a knowledge of the evolutionary history of man, and began an energetic search for more remains. In August 1936 he found an almost intact skull in a quarry near Sterkfontein, which he considered to belong to an adult specimen which he named *Australopithecus transvaalensis*. Later, however, he considered that it belonged to a new genus which he termed *Plesianthropus transvaalensis*. Two years later, in June 1938, not far from Kromdraai, he found another skull fragment, from which he described another type of *Australopithecus*, giving it the name *Paranthropus robustus*. In 1947 he resumed work at Sterkfontein. Following the finding of the skull of a semi-adult *Plesianthropus*, six well preserved teeth and a child's skull with a few milk teeth in it, came the most significant discovery of all, on April 18, 1947. On that day, with his assistant John Talbot, Broom found a splendidly preserved skull, lacking only the lower jaw and the teeth of the upper jaw. It was the skull a female *Plesianthropus*.

This female skull, which the newspapers promptly nicknamed 'Mrs Ples', and which was known unofficially by this name throughout the scientific world, caused the scientists to revise their views on the South African finds. Although Mrs Ples — with her massive, powerful jaws, which were slightly protracted into a snout, and her flattened nose — was no beauty, she nevertheless attracted the attention of many experts, who became ever more convinced that South Africa was the most important place in the world for the study of the origin of man's development.

In Swartkrans, about one and a half miles from Sterkfontein, Broom discovered the teeth and lower jaw of a new *Paranthropus*, which he named *Paranthropus crassidens*, since the teeth were about half as large again as those of *Paranthropus robustus*. Successful work in these excavations was also done by Broom's assistant, J. T. Robinson, who found two skulls, characterised by fore and aft bony ridges on the vault, over half an inch high, similar to, though smaller than, those found on the skull of male gorillas, and a jaw so similar to a human jaw that the being to whom it belonged was given the name *Telanthropus* (Greek *telos*: goal.)

Meanwhile Broom's investigations produced further important discoveries. He found an almost intact male *Plesianthropus* jaw, the canine of which was larger than human canines, but was worn down to the same extent as the other teeth; such wear of the canines had not previously been observed in anthropoid apes. On August 1, 1948, he discovered an almost complete pelvis which fully confirmed the assumption that these South African Australopithecinae walked in a comparatively erect manner. The pelvis was not absolutely human in type, nor that of an anthropoid ape, but a mixture of the two, nearer to the human form.

This period also includes the remarkable find of I. Kitching, a colleague of Professor Dart, who in September 1947, in Makapansgat, found the back of a skull with markedly human characteristics. Since traces of charcoal were found nearby, the creature concerned was named *Australopithecus prometheus*, as an indication that it was already familiar with fire. This view, however, is now known to be mistaken.

The South African Australopithecinae are the most important palaeontological discoveries of recent years. Their bones belong to over thirty individuals of different ages, including those of children, adolescents and adults. Detailed studies of these remains, for which we are chiefly indebted to Dart, Broom, Robinson and Le Gros Clark, show that the Australopithecinae must be classified in the highest mammalian family, the *Hominidae*, to which we also belong. Within this family they form the sub-family of the Australopithecinae.

The skull of the *Australopithecus* is simian in size and very similar to that of the chimpanzee. The face is foreshortened and the mouth is only slightly protracted into a snout. The position of the foramen magnum is almost the same as in man. This helps to confirm that he walked almost erect and that his hands were therefore human in form. This is also attested to by the form of the pelvis, while the socket of the head of the femur is similar in form and position to that of man. The size of the cranial cavity is relatively small. In *Australopithecus africanus*, which is that of a young creature, the capacity of the cranium is only 450 c.c.; it is estimated that in an adult it would be about 650 c.c., which is less than half the average size of the human brain, but more than that of the largest gorilla. The size of the cranial cavity of *Plesianthropus* is about 560 c. c., and in the case of *Paranthropus robustus* about 650 c. c. That of the giant species *Paranthropus crassidens* is estimated at 900 c. c. in females and 1,000 c. c. in males. With the exception of the last-named species, therefore, the brain was only slightly larger than that of the present-day anthropoid apes. This shows that in the course of evolution the body was first raised to an erect position and the form of the limbs and teeth changed, while the size of the brain remained practically unaltered.

Today it is known that all Australopithecinae were much closer to man than to anthropoid apes.

The form and size of the incisors and canines are human, while the premolars and molars are larger than human. As already mentioned, the middle of the vault of some skulls is crossed by a bony ridge, like that possessed by male gorillas. In some of the lower jaws, incipient signs of a chin can be seen. The arrangement of the teeth is completely human in type, and the same applies to the form of the pelvis — with the exception of the hip-bone. These features indicate that *Paranthropus crassidens* was a highly specialised type and that it was probably a lateral branch of the Australopithecinae. *Telanthropus capensis* also occupies a special place, as seen from certain features of its lower jaw. In some respects it resembles the Heidelberg jaw, in others it is similar to *Paranthropus*. It thus occupies a place between *Protanthropus* and *Paranthropus*. There are many expert opinions as to its exact position in the chain, some including it among the Prehominidae, but whichever view is correct, it is evident that *Telanthropus* must be regarded as a very primitive kind of 'human' form.

The Australopithecinae are close to man not only as regards their skeletal structure, but also as regards some of their habits, brought to light quite recently. Among the broken bones and skulls of animals, Dart also found a number of skulls of Australopithecinae which had been broken by blows, some administered vertically from the front, others aimed at the left temple. Dart regards this as evidence of intentional killing, and hence of cannibalism. This is a human rather than simian characteristic, since monkeys do not kill each other for food. Moreover, in October 1954, C.K. Brain discovered 129 worn stones in Makapansgat, seventeen of which were identified by C. van Riet Lowe as very primitive implements. Since one year later A. R. Hughes discovered a fragment of the jaw of an *Australopithecus* in the immediate vicinity, it seems likely that the implements were produced by Australopithecinae; this, of course, is one of the special abilities of all Hominids.

The Australopithecinae are undoubtedly of great evolutionary significance. The only thing which prevents them from being regarded as direct ancestors of man is their relatively late geological date. South African research workers like to date them as Tertiary finds, but they all appear to date actually from the early Quaternary when *Pithecanthropus*, *Sinanthropus*, *Protanthropus* and other similar forms already existed. The Australopithecinae cannot, therefore, be their ancestors, and are probably old, surviving forms, differing only slightly from the true forms of man's primaeval ancestors. Professor von Koenigswald is probably right in assuming that the human group in the broadest sense — the Hominidae — broke away from the anthropoid apes, already in very ancient times, without at first showing any fundamental differences from the group which fathered the present-day anthropoid apes. Within this group there appeared a branch — possibly the Australopithecinae — which developed roughly parallel with the anthropoid ape group, differentiated, however, by a more erect manner of walking and by having fewer canine teeth. A further offshoot of this branch, characterised, in the course of evolution, mainly by fewer teeth and the growth of a brain, developed into man.

The Australopithecinae lived about 900,000 to 300,000 years ago. As a result of their discovery it seems likely that the place of man's origin was Central Africa, which was the point from which the first human beings spread far and wide.

# THE QUATERNARY –
# THE AGE OF HUMAN LIFE

It is interesting to consider what the world looked like when the first true human beings appeared in it. This was at the end of the Tertiary. The warm climate everywhere began slowly to deteriorate, and this naturally affected the development of plants and animals. This drop in temperature reached a climax at the beginning of the Quaternary. The early Quaternary or Pleistocene period is also known as the Ice Age. There were two forms of glaciation; in the mountains glaciers were formed, while the extremes of both the northern and southern hemispheres were covered with ice-sheets. The mountain glaciers were either newly formed, or existing glaciers increased in size, descending into the valleys or covering large areas of foothills. At the time of its maximum extent, the Alpine glacier stretched to the foot of the Black Forest and to the Upper Danube.

The continental ice-sheets were much bigger. In Europe, an enormous sheet spread out from the mountains of Scandinavia in all directions. At the time of its maximum extent it covered the whole of Fennoscandia and stretched north-east across the northern Urals as far as the river Ob, where it merged with the North Siberian ice-sheet. To the south-east it extended as far as the Volga, to Kiev, and thence to Galicia, Przemyśl and the Beskydy mountains; one tongue reached out to the Moravian Gate, then on past the Sudeten area to the Harz, the lower Rhine and Britain, which it covered except for the southern parts, passing north via Iceland and Greenland. At one time this ice-sheet covered over six million square kilometres, or two and a quarter million square miles. In North America another ice-sheet covered almost the whole of Canada and part of Alaska, reaching deep into the United States, as far as the Ohio and Missouri. The extent of this sheet has been estimated at ten million square kilometres, or almost four million square miles.

The Ice Age lasted almost from the beginning of the Quaternary for the whole of the Pleistocene period, almost one million years, certainly not less than 700,000 years. Its course was not the same throughout. True glacial periods, with low temperatures and abundant atmospheric condensation, alternated with interglacial periods, during which the weather in our own latitudes was often warmer than it is today. During the interglacial periods, the rise in temperature caused the glaciers to retreat and the ice-sheet to recede to the north.

Penck and Brückner recognised four glacial periods in the Alps, which they named according to streams flowing northwards from the Alps into Würtemberg and Bavaria, and forming the right tributaries of the Danube. These are the Günz, Mindel, Riss and Würm periods, of which the Mindel period was the longest. This classification of Alpine glaciation has been generally adopted, and has recently been elaborated in detail to become the basis of division of the Pleistocene.

According to the terminal moraines — the deposits of debris at the ends of the glaciers — three glacial periods were determined for the northern ice-sheet which moved southwards over the Baltic and North Germany. These were likewise named by the three rivers marking their limits. The oldest was the Elster period, corresponding in time to the Alpine Mindel period. The next was the Saale period, when the ice extended roughly as far as a line from Dresden to Dortmund, and the third was the Weichsel period. It is interesting to note that a period corresponding to the oldest Alpine Günz period was long unknown in the north, but in 1937 Richter discovered traces of a 'Baltic ice-sheet', which he thought probably corresponded to the Günz period. Nevertheless, the time from the end of the Tertiary to the Mindel glacial period in the north of Central Europe and North Germany is still described as the preglacial period.

The extent of the glaciers and ice-sheets also changed during the individual glacial periods. The first three Alpine glacial periods had two such fluctuations, the last had three. The warmer intervals between the cold waves of the same glacial period are known as interstadials.

In tropical and subtropical regions it is believed that there were pluvials, periods of torrential rainfall, separated by dry periods known as interpluvials.

During the glacial periods the climate was very harsh and dry, as the slow but steady cooling caused a big drop in the annual temperature. The frosts converted the surface layers of rock to drift, which was carried along by the advancing ice. In regions not covered with ice, the rivers froze during the winter, while in the summer, the water carried the drift away, wearing it down into boulders and pebbles. This drift, most of which came from the terminal moraine, was deposited in the river beds, so that the rivers aggraded their valleys with sediments. These are known as fluvioglacial deposits. The dry, cold winds blowing across the ice dried the soil and from the large sandy deposits in front of the glacier and from free moraines it carried away the fine, buff-coloured dust. This dust, rich in calcium carbonate and soil components, is known as loess; it settled elsewhere, forming coherent layers, loose, porous, rich in valuable nutrients and hence very fertile. The increase in the size of the river valleys and the formation of loess were the outcome of the glacial period.

The alternation of glacial and interglacial periods, over long intervals, had an important effect upon the flora and fauna of the regions involved. During the glacial periods, the regions which were covered by the ice-sheet were completely destitute of vegetation. In periglacial areas — regions one or two hundred miles in advance of the northern ice-sheet — there were three distinguishable belts of vegetation; tundra, steppe and taiga.

At the edge of the melting ice, from which sprang hundreds of dirty little streams, grew plants which still flourish in the boundless tundra in the most northerly regions of Europe and Asia. Chief among them were different species of moss and lichens, such as reindeer moss (*Cladonia rangifera*) and the large, flat cushions of *Dryas octopetala* with its white flowers. Together with these bloomed the saxifrage (*Saxifraga oppositifolia*) and dwarf azalea (*Azalea procumbens*). Stunted willows, such as the dwarf willow (*Salix herbacea*) formed thick growths, together with creepers. The dwarf birch (*Betula nana*), which scarcely rose above the wet soil, grew together with lichens and peat-mosses on the banks of icy pools and rivers.

Further south the tundra gradually gave way to grassy steppe, where willows and birches, juniper trees and flowering heather grew among the luxuriant grass. In some places dwarf pines (*Pinus montana* and *Pinus silvestris*) appeared. Beyond the steppe, with its cold, dry climate, came the taiga, characterised by coniferous and deciduous forests and a warmer, damper climate.

Whenever the continental ice-sheet retreated northwards, the climate grew warmer and warmth-loving vegetation moved from south to north. At the same time mountain flora moved up the sides of mountains in the wake of the retreating glaciers. Thus the alternation of glacial and interglacial periods had a great influence on the flora of Europe, though the transition of glacial to interglacial flora was very gradual. If this process is observed in some of the profiles of interglacial deposits, it is found that layers containing typical tundra flora are followed in the first place by deposits containing the remains of pine (*Pinus silvestris*) and birch (*Betula alba*), and then by spruce (*Picea excelsa*), fir (*Abies pectinata*) and aspen (*Populus tremula*). Next came deciduous forests with varied undergrowth, representing the climax of the interglacial increase in temperature in Central Europe. The main trees were the oak (*Quercus robur* and *Quercus sessilifera*), beech (*Fagus silvatica*), lime (*Tilia platyphyllos* and *Tilia parviflora*), maple (*Acer platanoides* and *Acer campestris*), sycamore (*Acer pseudoplatanus*), ash (*Fraxinus excelsior*), hornbeam (*Carpinus betulus*), alder (*Alnus glutinosa*), hazel (*Corylus avellana*), hawthorn (*Crataegus oxyacantha*), and others. As a new glacial period approached, first the oak and beech woods disappeared, then the spruce, birch and pine woods, until development was again completed by the appearance of tundra flora.

As with the flora, changes naturally occurred similarly in the fauna. During the earliest Pleistocene, in the Villefranchian period, the mastodons, which had been so typical for the Tertiary, were almost extinct. Their place was taken by the fossil elephants *Elephas* (in the latest terminology, *Archidiskodon*)

27

*planifrons* and *Elephas* (*Archidiskodon*) *meridionalis*, accompanied by the fossil rhinoceros *Dicerorhinus etruscus* and the primitive zebra-like quaggas of the genus *Allohippus*. In place of extinct antelopes and gazelles came the first giant deer (*Megaceros* sp.).

Soon, however, the northern ice-sheet began to advance southwards, the glaciers descended, and the tundra, steppe and taiga made their first appearance in Europe. After a time they disappeared, only to return. The tundra was always inhabited by two types of animals — northern (Arctic) animals, driven south by the ice-sheet, and mountain (Alpine) animals, driven to lower levels by the glaciers. This mixture is known as Arcto-Alpine fauna. The commonest animals in the tundra were lemmings (*Myodes torquatus*, *Myodes obensis*, etc.), the varying hare (*Lepus variabilis*), followed by the polar fox (*Alopex lagopus*), which played havoc in their ranks, together with the predatory wolverine (*Gulo gulo*), which also hunted larger animals. Commonest among the birds were the ptarmigan (*Lagopus albus*) and the Alpine grouse (*Lagopus mutus*).

The scanty flora of the tundra also nourished large animals, including the reindeer (*Rangifer tarandus* and *Rangifer arcticus*) and the enormous musk-ox (*Ovibos moschatus*), a hollow-horned ruminant forming a kind of link between sheep and cattle, and still extant in parts of North America. The chamois (*Rupicapra tragus*), the ibex (*Capra ibex*) and the marmot (*Marmota marmota*) were driven down from the mountains.

Fluctuations in climate resulted in the frequent invasion of the tundra by the steppe, so that tundra and steppe fauna are sometimes found together. Alongside the small animals which enlivened the steppe, such as the steppe marmot (*Marmota bobac*) and the ground squirrel (*Citellus citellus*) and different species of hamsters and voles, lived the skunk, weasel, ermine, chamois, ibex, wild horse, bison, aurochs, mammoth and hairy rhinoceros. Wooded areas were inhabited chiefly by red deer, roe-deer and fallow-deer. Many beasts of prey also roamed the steppes and the forests, the most dangerous being the lion, bear, hyaena, wolf and lynx.

In the warm interglacial periods wooded regions were inhabited by the fossil elephant, fossil rhinoceros, forest bison, a peculiar species of wild horse (*Equus germanicus*) with a large head and teeth but narrow face, bears, wolves, wild cats, beavers and other animals. During the first interglacial period, the hippopotamus (*Hippopotamus maior*) was still to be found in Britain and the Rhineland.

Some species lived both in glacial and interglacial periods, including the wolf, cave bear and brown bear, cave hyaena and cave lion.

The fauna of the individual glacial and interglacial periods differed in many respects. Mention should be made of at least some of the general characteristics of the fauna of the periods when the first true human beings — *Homo neanderthalensis* and *Homo sapiens fossilis* — lived. It will be sufficient to mention only the larger mammals, starting from the second interglacial period, since geologically the oldest truly human remains — the Steinheim skull — belong to the third glacial period.

The second continental (Mindel) ice-sheet melted and retreated northwards, to be followed by the second interglacial period, which lasted almost 200,000 years. The forest limits, which during the Mindel period had been pushed far to the south, somewhere in the Balkans, again moved northwards, together with the warmth-loving fauna. They had undergone evolutionary changes, however, since being driven south by the glacial period. The preglacial fossil forest elephant *Elephas* (*Archidiskodon*) *meridionalis* had become the fossil forest elephant of the interglacial periods, *Elephas* (*Palaeoloxodon*) *antiquus*, which was often accompanied in Central Europe by the fossil rhinoceros *Coelodonta antiquitatis* (or *Dicerorhinus kirchenbergensis*). Newcomers appeared like the buffalo (*Buffelus murrensis*), and the aurochs (*Bos primigenius*). Both emigrated from their home in South Asia and settled near rivers and swamps in Central Europe. From the same parts came the giant deer of the species *Cervus megaceros antecedens* (now termed *Megaceros giganteus antecedens*) and other giant deer of the *Dolichodoryceros* tribe. Fallow-deer (*Dama*), red deer (*Cervus elaphus*), roe-deer (*Capreolus capreolus*) and the wild boar (*Sus scrofa*) also returned to Europe. The quaggas were replaced by true wild horses of the genus *Equus*, large herds living in the grassy areas of different regions. Other animals were terrorised by beasts of prey, the lion still being found in Central Europe at that time.

The third (Riss) glacial period was then ushered in, and lasted over 40,000 years. Once again tundra and Alpine fauna advanced before the ice and settled in the broad plains of Central Europe. The forests retreated far to the south, taking with them the warmth-loving animals. The mammoth (*Elephas* or *Mammonteus primigenius*) was quite different from the old steppe mammoth (*Parelephas trogontherii*) of preglacial times. The mammoth was accompanied by the hairy rhinoceros (*Coelodonta antiquitatis*), the reindeer (*Rangifer tarandus*), the musk ox (*Ovibos moschatus*) and a host of smaller animals, such as the ibex (*Capra camburgensis*), the steppe fox (*Vulpes corsac*), the wolverine (*Gulo gulo*), and others. The further the ice advanced south, the further these northern tundra penetrated into Central Europe. South of this area, i.e. in the part between the periglacial zone in the north and the Alpine ice in the south, lived the wild horse (*Equus germanicus*), the bison (*Bison priscus*), the red deer (*Cervus elaphus*), the gigantic *Cervus megaceros germaniae*, the wolf (*Lupus lupus*), the cave bear (*Ursus spelaeus*), the cave lion (*Felis,* or *Panthera spelaea*), together with the mammoth and the hairy rhinoceros.

After the Riss glacial period a gradual change in the climate ushered in the last of the interglacial periods, which lasted 70,000 years. The forest boundaries again shifted northwards, and with them came the fossil elephant and fossil rhinoceros, the fallow-deer, the red deer, the aurochs and the wild boar. The open grassy plains were the haunt of the wild horse and the giant deer.

The ice attacked again for the last time. The fourth glacial period lasted 90,000 years. The fossil elephant and rhinoceros died out, and into the empty spaces of Central Europe emerged the cold-loving animals such as the mammoth, the hairy rhinoceros and the reindeer. Somewhat further south lived the wild horse, the red deer, the bison, the aurochs and others. Beasts of prey were numerous, especially the cave lion, cave hyaena and cave bear.

The last glacial period came to an end, however, concluding the Pleistocene, the oldest period of the Quaternary. It was followed by the postglacial period, also known as the *Alluvium* or *Holocene*. In Europe, the tundra disappeared, the steppes were soon overgrown with thickets and woods, which in time became endless forests, stretching far to the north. As the ice retreated, the mammoth and hairy rhinoceros also moved further north, where they soon died out. In the wake of the ice-sheet came herds of reindeer, with small cold-loving animals. Europe was gradually populated by the same fauna and flora which it still possesses, apart from a few alterations, today.

One more thing requires mentioning — the topography of the continents and seas in the Pleistocene period. The British Isles still formed part of the European mainland, since the English Channel was formed only in the postglacial period. The Rhine flowed into the North Sea at a point much further north than it does today, and the Thames was one of its tributaries. Spitzbergen was still attached to Scandinavia. The North Sea was much smaller than it is today and Scotland, Jan Mayen Island, Iceland and Greenland were probably all connected, and only separated during the Pleistocene period. This gave the Gulf Stream another course, so that its warming influence was not then felt in North-West Europe.

The Mediterranean was much the same in form and appearance as it is today. The straits of Gibraltar already existed, but at the beginning of the Quaternary, Corsica, Sardinia and Elba were probably still joined to the mainland near Toulon and Nice. It is also possible that Sicily and Malta were connected to Africa. At this time the Mediterranean did not yet communicate with the Black Sea, which was an enormous inland lake, partially connected with the Caspian Sea. The communication between the Black Sea and the Mediterranean was formed only during the postglacial period.

The topography of the other continents and seas has also not changed much since the beginning of the Quaternary. At that time Japan and the East Indies still formed part of the Asian mainland, Africa was finally separated from Asia by subsidence of the present Red Sea area, and the Mediterranean communicated for a time with the Indian Ocean, the Suez divide being formed later. At the beginning of the Pleistocene, North America and Asia were separated, though they were possibly joined for a short time in the region of the Bering Strait, at the start of the postglacial period. Australia and its attendant islands were completely separated from Asia throughout the whole of the Quaternary.

# DIVISION OF THE QUATERNARY

| | Alpine (after Benck-Brückner) | | North German | Chronological extent |
|---|---|---|---|---|
| **Holocene (alluvium)** | Present day | | Present day | 0 |
| | Postglacial period | | Postglacial period | — 18,000 |
| **Pleistocene (diluvium)** — Late | IVth glacial period (Würm) | Würm 3 *(interstadial ²/₃)* Würm 2 *(interstadial ½)* Würm 1 | IVth glacial period (Weichsel) | — 25,000 — 72,000 — 115,000 |
| | 3rd interglacial period (Riss-Würm) | | *3rd interglacial period* (Weichsel-Saale) | |
| Middle | IIIrd glacial period (Riss) | Riss 2 *(interstadial ½)* Riss 1 | IIIrd glacial period (Saale) | — 187,000 — 230,000 |
| | 2nd interglacial period (Mindel-Riss) | | *2nd interglacial period* (Saale-Elster) | |
| | IInd glacial period (Mindel) | Mindel 2 *(interstadial ½)* Mindel 1 | IInd glacial period (Elster) | — 425,000 — 476,000 |
| Early | 1st interglacial period (Günz-Mindel) | | | |
| | Ist glacial period (Günz) | Günz 2 *(interstadial ½)* Günz 1 | Preglacial period | — 550,000 — 590,000 |
| | Villafranche period (earliest pleistocene) | | | — 700,000 to 1,000,000 years |

Tertiary — late (Neogene): Pliocene, Miocene — early (Palaeogene): Oligocene, Eocene, Palaeocene — 54,000,000 years

In some tables, another glacial period — the 'Danube period' — is placed before the Ist (Günz) glacial period, followed by the Danube-Günz interglacial period. Three stadials are sometimes given for the IIIrd (Riss) glacial period (Riss 1, Riss 2, Riss 3), with two interstadials (½, ²/₃).

# STONE, THE FOUNDATION
# OF HUMAN CULTURE

Who would have thought that human culture was founded on plain stone? Such, nevertheless, is the case. Stone was man's first aid in the struggle for existence and is an accurate guide in tracing his slowly developing culture. Stone was the first symbol of man's power, his first tool and his first weapon.

Stone implements fashioned by man or his forebears are found in Early Pleistocene rocks, the oldest being 500,000 to 600,000 years old. They were not, however, immediately recognised as such. In the 1830's, Boucher de Perthes, customs officer and archaeologist, found a number of flints in gravels of the river Somme, near Abbeville in Normandy. They appeared to be shaped artificially and to have been primitive implements and weapons. When, in 1839, Boucher de Perthes submitted his finds to scientists in Paris as tools and weapons of Pleistocene man, he was met with derision instead of understanding.

Despite this he went ahead and published a work of five volumes on his discoveries, which provoked controversy on all sides. His opponents stated that it was impossible for a provincial amateur of antiques to understand science, that his stone implements were forgeries, and that his book should be banned if only because it was contrary to the teaching of the Church on the creation of man. Boucher's fight with his adversaries lasted fifteen years, until two British scientists, Lyell and Prestwich, came to his aid. They made a careful study of Boucher's collection and finally declared his discoveries to be genuine. It was mainly Sir Charles Lyell's book, *Geological Evidence of the Antiquity of Man*, published in London in 1863, which silenced Boucher's opponents. It is now established that these primitive tools and weapons were made in what is known as the Palaeolithic, or Old Stone Age.

The South African Australopithecinae were, as far as we yet know, the first to use sharp-edged stones or pointed fragments of bone as implements and weapons. It is also possible that some of these early human beings who were more advanced were able to fashion rough instruments. The finds of Brain, Lowe and Hughes show that this was probably the case. Neanderthal Man, however, went much further than his predecessors in the art of making stone implements and weapons. When he discovered the many advantages of a sharp-pointed stone, he probably realised that this would help him to overcome numerous problems; later, when he discovered that cracked and broken stones had sharp edges and were frequently hollow, he must have been struck by the numerous possible uses of flint fragments. Much ingenuity and hard work must have been required, however, before the desired result was obtained.

The best materials for producing implements and weapons were flint and hornstone. If these were not available, Palaeolithic Man often had to use less suitable material, such as quartz, quartzite, siliceous sandstone or limestone, according to his environment. These tools and weapons were never as effective, however, as flints.

Two types of stone industry are distinguished, according to the manner in which the implements were fashioned: core — formed from a solid piece of flint, quartz or other stone, from which flakes were struck off; and flakes — in which the detached fragments were used.

Since the Palaeolithic was extremely long and the technique of the formation of stone implements and weapons passed through numerous stages of development, the stone industry is used as the basis of the classification of man's cultural development at that time. Since France was inhabited even when large parts of Europe were still covered by the ice-sheet, the first and oldest classification systems come from France, and the individual types of culture were named after the places where they were found.

The earliest system was devised by G. de Mortillet in 1869, and although improved in some respects, must be regarded as the classic system. He divided the early Palaeolithic into the Chellean, Acheulian and Mousterian periods, and the later Palaeolithic into the Aurignacian, Solutrian and Magdalenian periods. All are differentiated by their different stone cultures. The modern classification is more involved, and is based on the discovery that during the early Palaeolithic, two separate cultures existed in Europe and Asia. The first was characterised chiefly by working on both sides of the stone (hand-axe, *coup de poing* culture) and is divided into the Chellean, Acheulian and Micoquian periods. Alongside this hand stone culture, which probably originated in Africa and then spread to Europe and South Asia, existed a second culture, characterised first by flake industry, with only few hand stones, and which also probably spread to Europe from Africa. This is divided chronologically into the Clactonian, Levalloisian, Tayacian and Mousterian periods, though some of these stages occasionally overlap. The modern classification of the later Palaeolithic is the same as the classic system, but subdivided and interstratified.

Both these classification systems are primarily applicable to France, although as far as their general principles are concerned, they can also be applied to Central Europe, where, as in other places, local cultures are found.

In order to clarify some of the terms used in this section it should be mentioned that every stone object fashioned by man or by his predecessors for a given purpose is called an artifact. Artifacts of the same age are known collectively as an industry. Culture is the collective term applied to the activity of a people as seen from their industry, and from other evidence of their mode of living. During the Palaeolithic, the various cultures are differentiated according to the variable methods used in fashioning stone implements, whilst during the Neolithic, the Later Stone Age, they are distinguished by the type of their ceramic products.

# NEANDERTHAL MAN PEOPLES THE WORLD

In Western Germany, near Düsseldorf, there is a picturesque little valley, which from 1674 to 1679 was the favourite haunt of Joachim Neander, an Evangelical theologian and rector of the Latin college in Düsseldorf. Since he was held in great esteem locally, the valley was named after him, and acquired international fame by conferring its name on a now extinct race of man, the Early Palaeolithic Neanderthal Man (*Homo neanderthalensis*).

In 1856, workers were quarrying limestone in this valley, which was riddled with cracks and caves. When they came to the so-called Feldhof cave, and began to clear the floor of soil, they found a large number of bones, which they threw down the steep slope to the bottom of the valley, together with the soil. The bones, which were salvaged by the owner of the quarry, were sent to Johann Carl Fuhlrott, a teacher at the grammar school in Elberfeld. Altogether, fourteen parts of the skeleton were saved — the skullcap (the most important part from the scientific aspect), both femora, humeri and radii, the right ulna, part of the left side of the pelvis, a fragment of a shoulder-blade, a section of the right collarbone and five rib fragments.

The Neanderthal find aroused keen interest among scientists, particularly when Fuhlrott, backed by the anatomist Schaaffhausen, declared at a congress of naturalists and doctors in Bonn in the spring of 1857, that the bones probably belonged to some extinct race of human beings. The delegates were thunderstruck, since it was the first time that they had been brought face to face with the problem of evolution, and it must be remembered that Darwin had not yet published his *Origin of Species*.

The first shock and indecision over the skeletal remains from the Neanderthal were soon succeeded by violent battle. Few scientists sided with Fuhlrott and Schaaffhausen. In 1872, the bones were submitted to Professor Rudolf Virchow of Berlin University, an acknowledged authority in the field of pathology. At a congress of anthropologists Virchow declared that the bones belonged to an unfortunate individual whose limbs had undergone numerous pathological changes; this individual was old, he had had severe rickets when young, and acute gout towards the end of his life. The bones could not possibly be regarded as those of a primitive human being.

Those who refused to accept Virchow's decision were soon to be heartened by a new discovery of similar remains in the Bec aux Roches cave near Spy, in Belgium. In this cave, Marcel de Puydt, Fraipont and de Lohest found two human skeletons together with a number of flint implements of the Mousterian period and many bones of Pleistocene animals, including the cave bear, the mammoth, the hairy rhinoceros, the aurochs and others. Both human skeletons, particularly the skulls, were exactly of the Neanderthal type. Thus two more individuals had been found of a type previously held to be an isolated example, differing only from the normal human type by pathological deformation of the bones. It was now evident that the Neanderthal specimen was a normal, healthy human being, but varying in form from contemporary man.

The Spy discoveries were also of great significance because of the accompanying stone implements, weapons and animal bones, which made it possible for experts to determine their geological age. It was demonstrated irrefutably that the prehistoric human beings of Spy had lived at the same time as the typical Pleistocene animals with whose bones their remains were discovered. What was mere assumption in the case of the Neanderthal discoveries was convincingly demonstrated by expert research where the Spy excavations were concerned. The entire controversy was resolved by the Strasbourg anatomist, Professor Gustav Schwalbe, in papers published between 1897 and 1904. He proved that the Neanderthal skull was normal and that its variation from that of present-day man was evolutionary, not pathological. After detailed studies, Klaatsch, Fraipont and de Lohest arrived at the same conclusions regarding the limb bones.

All further discoveries merely confirmed the views of these research workers. Neanderthal Man had definitely existed. Remains have since been unearthed in many countries, including Germany, Belgium, France, Croatia, Czechoslovakia, Spain, Palestine and the U.S.S.R.

## THE PICTURE OF NEANDERTHAL MAN

All bones found clearly show that the Neanderthal race was a developmentally lower type than later Palaeolithic Man (*Homo sapiens fossilis*) and present-day man (*Homo sapiens*). The most striking differences are in the skull, with its low, sharply receding forehead, thick supraorbital ridges, shallow cranial cavity and strong zygomatic arch, in which the powerful masseter muscles controlling the chinless lower jaw were inserted. From this latter characteristic it is widely assumed — though not definitely proved — that Neanderthal Man was not yet capable of coherent, articulate speech. The nape of the neck was long, with powerfully developed insertions for the neck muscles. The jaws tended to protrude. The teeth were large and strong, but already typically human. From finds of entire skeletons it may be concluded that Neanderthal Man was powerfully built, with an average height of 160 — 165 cm. (5 ft. 3in — 5 ft. 5 in.), and probably did not walk as erectly as we do today, but bending slightly forward.

In view of the primitive structure of the skull, which had some features in common with that of anthropoid apes, it is surprising to note from casts of the cranial cavity that the brain of some of these beings was actually larger than that of modern man. Individuals with a cranial capacity of over 1,600 c. c. include the original Neanderthal Man and those found in Spy, La Chapelle and La Ferrasie. In some instances, however, the cranial capacity was smaller, and the structure of the individual brain centres was more advanced than in those with a larger cranial capacity.

Comparing the brain of *Pithecanthropus* or *Sinanthropus* with that of an anthropoid ape such as an adult gorilla (the term 'brain' in this context also applying to a cast of the cranial cavity), shows that in the former types there is marked enlargement of the part of the brain responsible for higher mental activity, i.e. the frontal lobes. The frontal lobes also show discernible convolutions, providing convincing evidence of the development of the intelligence. Comparison of the brains of *Pithecanthropus* and Neanderthal Man shows further enlargement of all the important parts of the brain, chiefly involving the parietal, occipital and temporal lobes, but also including the frontal lobes. These were still influenced, however, by the low, flattened forehead.

The front of Neanderthal Man's brain was thus, in general, low and small, and the convolutions of the frontal lobes did not give the cerebral hemispheres the typical form made possible in modern man by his broad, high forehead. Since the frontal lobes were not fully developed, and since they are regarded as the centre for association of ideas, it is thought that Neanderthal Man's reasoning faculties may have been limited. This was compensated, however, by the development of his senses, as seen from the enlargement of the parietal, occipital and temporal lobes, all sensory centres.

It should not, however, be presumed that Neanderthal man was incapable of all thought and reasoning. His hard life compelled him to do so, even if his reflections were on a primitive level; and as, in the course of the ages, he used his mental faculties in increasing measure, resolving more difficult and complex problems, so the frontal lobes and low forehead began to increase in height. In some skulls mild signs of vaulting are, in fact, visible.

The brain of Neanderthal Man displays one other interesting feature, already observed in the brain of *Pithecanthropus*, namely that the left frontal lobe is slightly larger than the right. This is a sign of right-handedness, which may therefore be regarded as an old-established attribute of man, whether acquired by practice or by learning.

To sum up, it can be said that the brain of Neanderthal Man definitely shows progressive development, but that it also had deficiencies, and did not reach the characteristic level of its successors.

## THE LIFE OF NEANDERTHAL MAN

Discoveries in Neanderthal encampments have helped to explain when and how these people lived. It is now known that they lived mainly during the last interglacial period, and at the outset of the fourth glacial period. During the former they lived in the open, in encampments; during the latter, in caves.

They lived in small bands, feeding upon whatever they could gather or catch. They stalked and killed small game, and occasionally hunted large animals, for which they may have laid snares and traps. They cut up their quarry on the spot, taking back to camp only the choicest and most easily carried morsels, which they then roasted in the fire. If the animal was exceptionally large, such as the fossil elephant or fossil forest rhinoceros, they made several journeys. Evidence of this was found at Taubach, in Germany. Marrow was considered a delicacy, and the long bones were broken open to obtain it. The brain was also regarded as a titbit, and the skull was likewise cracked open.

In Europe, especially in Alpine regions, the favourite nourishment of Neanderthal Man was the flesh of the cave bear, and quantities of bones have been found in almost all their encampments. In Central Asia (Teshik-tash, Uzbekistan), they hunted the Siberian ibex, and the fact that they were able to pursue such swift and vigilant animals serves to show that they were clever and efficient hunters.

Because of their manner of obtaining food, they had to keep on the move. They continually changed their camping grounds, according to the state of the vegetation and the hunting conditions. It is possible that even then every community had its own site and hunting ground, which it defended against all intruders.

To protect themselves from cold and frost they covered their bodies with animal skins. Although their open-air life and its difficult conditions made them very hardy, they suffered from different diseases, chief among which was rheumatism, due to the long periods spent in damp caves. Their lives were also relatively short, since the skeletons of fifty-year-old males often showed clear signs of typical senility.

The implements and weapons of Neanderthal Man were chiefly of stone. One tool was the hand-axe, others included side and end scrapers and points, i.e. instruments suitable for cutting, scraping, engraving, boring, etc. Quartzite, limestone and other types of rock were employed in addition to flint, though flint instruments were the best. Used bones have also been discovered, fashioned mainly from the long bones of large animals such as the cave bear. The lower jaw of this animal, with its large canines, would be useful as a life-preserver.

Neanderthal Man left no works of art behind him, such as those characteristic of the mammoth and reindeer hunters, who succeeded him.

## THE MOUSTERIAN BURIALS

In 1908, the Swiss collector, Otto Hauser, discovered the grave of a young Neanderthal man, near the village of Le Moustier, in the valley of the river Vézère, in southern France. The skeleton lay on its right side, the right hand under its head and its legs drawn up. Beside the skeleton lay flint instruments, with a fine example of a hand-axe, and a number of animal bones, including burnt ones. A series of similar discoveries followed.

Burials of the Mousterian period are the oldest on record, and clearly show that Neanderthal Man was already preoccupied with the mysteries of life and death. The direct stimulus to these thoughts was provided by the death of a friend or relative, either from natural causes or by violence. Why had the body suddenly stopped moving? What had left it so that it lay motionless? Was it because breathing had stopped or because the blood had ceased to flow from the wounds? These problems were beyond Neanderthal Man's intelligence, but it was essential, nevertheless, for him to resolve his own relationship with the dead man. The dead went on living in some mysterious manner, and were probably capable of causing great misfortune. Hence the need to protect oneself against the dead, to bury them near the fire where they had lived, to cover them to prevent them from waking and leaving the cave. Possibly thoughts such as these impelled him to bury the dead in the position in which they rested after work or hunting, deep asleep by the fire.

Since stone implements and burnt bones were found in some graves, it can be assumed that Neanderthal Man already had some conception of a future existence, not much different from their present mode of living. This is probably why they placed stone tools and a little food in the grave.

Some authors do not consider that these were true burials, suggesting that the dead were simply laid in the earth, and that even this was not a regular custom, as otherwise many more skeletons would have been found. They claim that burial was essential because of the odour of the decomposing body, which was not only unpleasant for the cave dwellers, but might also attract beasts of prey. The choice was between burying the dead and leaving the cave.

It is difficult to agree entirely with this view. Neanderthal Man was a typical hunter and nomad, with no settled mode of life. The length of his stay in any given spot was dependent upon the amount of game and the abundance of plant life. If the food supply was poor, hunger drove him on.

The view that the dead were buried simply in order to avoid leaving a camping place is also unlikely. Apart from the fact that they never buried their dead in deep pits, but only in shallow graves, ten to twelve inches deep (so that the odour of decomposing flesh would penetrate the thin covering layer of soil), they could have disposed of the corpses much more simply, by throwing them into the water, down a fissure in the rocks or into a ravine. Many communities doubtless did so. It is important to remember that they were not a physically uniform race, and that habits and customs probably varied greatly. It is, nevertheless, an established fact that real graves have been found.

Another argument advanced against Neanderthal burials is that intentional burial is based on conceptions of death and after-life. Ritual burial involves belief in another world and the desire to perpetuate the memory of the dead. It is asserted that Neanderthal Man and even the later Palaeolithic hunters (*Homo sapiens fossilis*) were incapable of such highly developed mental activity.

This argument is not entirely acceptable, for Neanderthal Man, though admittedly primitive, already had a human brain and used it in a simple manner. His first reaction to the fact of death was doubtless fear, and it would seem natural to remove the dead as soon as possible, either by burial or by removal from the cave. But burial may often have been a mark of respect or friendship for an outstanding member of the community, to prevent him from falling prey to wild beasts; and love or compassion may also have been a motive. The man at Le Moustier was young, but a man found near La Chapelle aux Saints had, according to the signs in his bones, suffered many years from arthritis, and towards the end of his life could have been no more than a wreck, of no possible value to the community. Furthermore, he had suffered from severe suppuration of the jaw. Yet he was given burial, and compassion seems the likeliest reason. Moreover, the burial of children surely implies a bond of family affection. It would be illogical to assume that they were only physically human, devoid of reason, intelligence and sentiment.


## THE CANNIBALS OF KRAPINA


Compassion and respect for the dead, therefore, go far back into the annals of time; but so do opposing sentiments, and that is why cases of cannibalism have also been encountered among Neanderthal races.

In 1889, thirteen years after the discovery of the Spy skeletons, Professor Gorjanović-Kramberger of Zagreb University, a geologist, discovered a Neanderthal encampment in a small cave near the town of Krapina. One layer consisted of a large hearth containing bones, almost all of which were human.

Most of these had been broken and were burnt in varying degrees. They belonged to at least ten different individuals, adults and children.

Professor Gorjanovič-Kramberger realised that he had found the remains of one of the oldest cannibal feasts. The Krapina Neanderthalers were thus not always peaceful hunters and fruit-eaters, but also fratricides, who killed members of the tribe and ate them, roasting their flesh in the fire. But it would be wrong to imagine that this was a normal custom, for although signs of cannibalism have been detected elsewhere, no other such gruesome encampment has yet been discovered.

## THE NEANDERTHAL HUNTING-MAGIC CULT

In more recent years, many new and interesting discoveries have been made concerning the lives of the Neanderthal tribes who roamed the Alps and the distant mountains of Uzbekistan.

In 1917 — 1921, Bächler and Nigg began exploring the Drachenberg in the Swiss Engadine. At the summit of this mountain, which is over 7,500 feet high, is the entrance to a cave known as the Drachenloch (Dragon's Hole). The first cave, near the entrance, showed nothing of interest, but the second contained a surprising discovery. The light of their lamp revealed an artificially erected limestone wall, about thirty inches high, running almost the whole length of the left wall of the cave. Behind it they were amazed to find a store of cave bear bones in the fifteen-inch space between the limestone wall and the natural cave wall. Most of the bones were intact and in a good state of preservation. They were all long limb bones and skulls, and stored in an orderly manner. For example, three skulls lay side by side, in the same position and facing in the same direction.

Bächler and Nigg thought at first that this had once been a meat store, but since the limb bones lay so close together, it appeared that they must have been bare of meat before being placed in position. They then had the idea that these might be the relics of a religious ceremony, a Neanderthal bear cult, similar to cults still found today among primitive people of the north. The wide distribution of these cults shows that they are very old.

In view of the many examples of bear cults still existing today, it is not surprising that the Drachenloch discovery caused Bächler and Nigg to assume that they had found their birthplace, and further excavations confirmed this. In August, 1920, they found a special stone cist between the second and third caves, containing bear skulls, and a year later, in the third cave, they discovered a well-preserved cave bear skull. The lower jaw was missing and the right zygomatic arch had been gnawed. The strangest feature of the find, however, was that the femur of a young cave bear had been inserted through the zygomatic arch, and that two shinbones lay on either side of the skull. Closer inspection showed that all four bones belonged to different animals.

Furthermore, in an alcove, between large boulders which had long ago fallen from the roof, lay a number of unmarred cave bear skulls, obviously a storage room. These finds convinced Bächler and Nigg that parts of the Drachenloch were actually the oldest ritual halls and shrines in the world.

The Drachenloch finds were followed by others. Artificial collections of cave bear skulls, sometimes together with the long limb bones, were found in other caves, such as the Petershöhle near Welden in Germany, the Wildenmannisloch cave in Switzerland, the Drachenhöhle near Mixnitz in Austria, etc.

All these discoveries, if correctly identified and explained, clearly confirm that they are precious relics of activities of Neanderthal hunters, associated with their hunting magic. There is of course no information about the actual rites, but it may be assumed that the ceremonies were fairly simple, and performed with dead animals.

Until quite recently it was thought that the Neanderthal bear cult was the only ancient hunting-magic cult in existence, but a discovery by the Leningrad prehistorian, A. P. Okladnikov, showed that this was not the case. In June, 1938, Okladnikov established a base on a high mountain near the village of Machai, for the purpose of prehistoric research. In the cave of Teshik-tash, he found the grave, partially destroyed by a small beast of prey, of a Neanderthal boy aged eight or nine years. The boy's head was surrounded by horns of the Siberian ibex, completely in fragments. Two pairs were still firmly joined to fragments of the frontal bones. The sharp points of the horns had been driven into the ground, the ends were at the same level as the skull. It was plainly a ritual burial. Other bones collected in the same cultural level were identified as belonging to the Siberian ibex, which convinced Okladnikov that the main quarry of the Teshik-tash hunters was the Siberian ibex.

Both this animal and the cave bear were of such great economic importance to the Neanderthalers that they soon influenced their entire lives and led, at least in some communities, to the growth of these special hunting-magic cults. Yet these were apparently not the only ones. Okladnikov drew attention to this in a brief account of a Neanderthal skull found in the Guattari cave on Monte Circeo in Italy. The skull, which was found in 1939, lay in a low cave, surrounded by a ring of stones, all approximately the same size. Professor Sergi, who made a detailed study of this discovery, supposed that the skull was the relic of a ritual burial, in which only the head was buried, while the rest of the body was eaten. Okladnikov also inclines to this view and assumes that the ring of stones might in some way be associated with the sun. It is more likely, however, that the cult concerned was a 'head' or 'skull' cult, rather than evidence of sun worship.

An account of the Neanderthal hunting-magic cults would be incomplete if no mention were made of the doubts cast upon them by some research workers. Certainly some of the views expressed in discussions on these cults are untenable, such as the explanation that the cave bear skulls represented hunting trophies. Neanderthal Man hunted for his living, not for sport or amusement. It is also a mistake to relate modern bear cults automatically to those of prehistoric times, as it is to exaggerate the importance of the link between Neanderthal Man and the animals he hunted. But it would be equally foolish to reject wholesale all views on Neanderthal cults, which are supported by abundant evidence.

## NEANDERTHAL MAN CONTROLS FIRE

The Neanderthal people already knew how to use fire, though we do not know how they eventually managed to tame it. We can imagine their terror, however, when the last spark vanished, taking with it the only hope of finding warmth and of roasting their meat. As darkness fell, fear filled their hearts, with no more flames to chase away the shadows or to keep away the wild beasts. Tending the fire must have been an extremely responsible duty.

When Neanderthal Man learned the secret of making fire, humanity took a great leap forward. It meant that man had harnessed one of the forces of nature for his own needs. The control of fire, the making of implements, and speech — these are exclusively human achievements. All man's other properties could have been inherited from his lower progenitors. Neanderthal Man certainly possessed the first two of these abilities, and was thus a true human being, although his body still showed signs of his origin.

## NEANDERTHAL MAN PEOPLES THE WORLD

After 1856, when the bones of Neanderthal Man were found in the Feldhof cave, many new discoveries of remains of this race were reported in Germany, France, Belgium and elsewhere. In Germany, important finds were made in Ehringsdorf and in Taubach near Weimar. One of the most important was made in 1933 in Steinheim, near Stuttgart. In France, the most significant finds were those of Le Moustier, La Chapelle aux Saints, Le Ferrasie, La Quina, Malarnaud, La Niche, etc. In Belgium, apart from the famous Spy discovery, others were made at La Naulette, near Furfooz. The most important find in Spain was the first discovery ever of a Neanderthal skull; this was at Gibraltar as far back as 1848. In Italy the relics of Saccopastore near Rome, and of the Guattari cave on Monte Circeo, are world famous.

Remains have also been found in the island of Jersey, in Yugoslavia (Krapina), Czechoslovakia (Šipka cave near Štramberk, Švédův stůl cave near Brno, and Gánovce near Poprad in Slovakia), Hungary (Subalyuk cave near Miskolc), and in the European part of the U.S.S.R. (Kiik-Koba and Staroselye caves in the Crimea).

Neanderthal Man also lived in Asia, and their traces have been found in Turkey, Iran, Palestine and Soviet Central Asia. There are, however, no traces of them in North or South America. The first human beings to set foot in America belonged to *Homo sapiens fossilis*, and probably arrived during the Mesolithic or Middle Stone Age, about 10,000 to 15,000 years ago. It would also be vain to search for traces of Neanderthal Man in Australia, as this continent has been separated from all the others by wide tracts of water for countless geological ages.

This geographical distribution of Neanderthal Man gives us no information about the density of their population in individual regions. In all the places previously mentioned, their bones have actually been found. Elsewhere, their open stations have been excavated, together with the hearth, and with used bones or stone implements. When considering the density of their populations in various countries, therefore, account should also be taken of those finds without bony relics.

## THE NEANDERTHALERS AND MAN'S FAMILY TREE

It is now known that the Neanderthalers, or their immediate ancestors, lived in Europe during the second (Mindel-Riss) interglacial period, and the classical type during the third (Riss-Würm) interglacial period and at the commencement of the fourth (Würm) glacial period. They thus covered an enormous time span. They also covered a large area of the earth's surface, and both factors are of great importance in an evaluation of their evolutionary significance.

At one time, when the only known find from Java was *Pithecanthropus erectus*, and only a few remains of Neanderthal Man and later Palaeolithic man (*Homo sapiens fossilis*) had been found in Western Europe, it was assumed that modern man had developed by way of *Pithecanthropus* and Neanderthal Man. This simple scheme of evolution has since been found to be somewhat more complicated.

Before the excavation of numerous relics of Neanderthal Man, it was believed that there was one uniform, distinct race, and some scientists considered that it was capable of further development. It appeared to them that Neanderthal Man developed in a direction which led to the formation of a clumsy, massive skeleton far removed from the finely modelled, lighter frame of later Palaeolithic man, our direct ancestor. Thus they regarded Neanderthal Man as merely an extinct side-branch.

More recent discoveries refuted this view of the uniformity of the Neanderthal race, by drawing attention to its wide geographical and chronological distribution and its range of variations, among which forms with many features similar to those of *Homo sapiens* have been found. The bones of some specimens show clearly discernible sapient features, i.e. features characteristic of later Palaeolithic man and modern man. The most important examples are the remains found at Steinheim, at Swanscombe in England, in Palestine, etc. At Staroselye in the Crimea, sapient features actually predominated in the skull of a Neanderthal child. It was also noted that some of these finds were geologically older than typical Neanderthal discoveries. Some research workers are therefore of the opinion that Neanderthalers with sapient features do not belong to the true, or classic type of Neanderthal Man, but that they form a special group, the presapient group. This was, therefore, an independent evolutionary group, leading directly to the *Homo sapiens fossilis* type, without passing through the Neanderthal stage. According to this opinion, the classic Neanderthalers are only a parallel evolutionary branch and have nothing to contribute towards the higher development of man, but the possibility of the crossing of Neanderthal and pre-sapient forms is not excluded.

Other scientists, with whom the author agrees, include the Neanderthalers with sapient features together with the classic Neanderthalers in one group, termed *Palaeanthropini* (Primaeval Man). Since it is now clear that they were not an uniform race, it would be more correct to speak of the Neanderthaloid group, rather than of the Neanderthal race. In this connection they are not regarded as an insignificant evolutionary group, but as the representatives of the pre-sapient group, from which sapient man (*Neanthropini*) developed. The representatives of the other group of Neanderthalers, who lived during the last interglacial period and at the beginning of the last glacial period, i.e. classic Neanderthalers, also differ in some respects. For example, the bones of Mediterranean Neanderthalers belonging to this group never show such marked, extreme features as the West European Neanderthalers of the Würm period, who also extended into Central and Eastern Europe. These West European Neanderthalers are rightly not regarded as the progenitors of later Palaeolithic man.

Considering Neanderthal Man and his evolutionary significance in this light, it can be said that living conditions and environment played an important part in his development. In regions near the ice-sheet, where life was difficult, the Neanderthalers developed into the typical, classic form. In these areas the progress of their evolution was slow and always in the same direction, thus intensifying and emphasising their characteristic features. This group of highly specialised classic types proved, indeed, to be a side-branch, which finally became extinct. The non-typical, sapient Neanderthalers, however, who lived far from the ice-sheet under more favourable conditions, were able to develop more easily and more rapidly, and at an earlier date, into a higher type of human being, more graceful in form and endowed with a higher intelligence. The finer bones of many of these Neanderthalers, their prominent forehead and other features are likely evidence of the development of sapient Neanderthal Man into the later type of *Homo sapiens fossilis*.

This transformation did not necessarily take place simultaneously and evenly in different parts of the world, but probably occurred wherever the conditions were favourable. At the same time, bordering groups doubtless mixed, resulting in increasing hereditary fixation of the more advantageous sapient features. The first to submit this explanation of the evolutionary significance of Neanderthal Man, in broad outline, was the Italian scientist, S. Sergi, later joined by others. Sergi was thus the first to support the theory of the Neanderthal phase in the evolution of man expressed by Aleš Hrdlička. The latter expressed this view in 1927 at a ceremony held in honour of Thomas Huxley, who in his own day had fought uncompromisingly for recognition of the evolutionary history of man, and the existence of Neanderthal Man. Hrdlička drew attention to the great variability of the Neanderthal race, and showed that there were no fundamental differences between the lives and cultures of Neanderthal Man and his later Palaeolithic successors, except that the former were more primitive.

New discoveries and revised opinions on older finds also lead to new theories on the subject. G. Heberer submitted the 'unfolding' hypothesis (Entfaltungshypothese), in which he claims that the origin of later Palaeolithic man should be sought neither among Neanderthal Man nor among presapient forms. He asserts that towards the end of the Tertiary, an anthropoid ape group split up into many forms, some of which gave rise to *Pithecanthropus*, *Sinanthropus*, etc., to Neanderthal Man, and to the modern type of man. These branches developed relatively independently of one another, and the only remaining product of the process is *Homo sapiens*, as the direct descendant of *Homo sapiens fossilis*.

Some research workers include the female skullcap from Ehringsdorf near Weimar in the pre-sapient group. It probably belongs to the peak of the last (Riss-Würm) interglacial period. In addition to Neanderthal features it possesses others (vaulted forehead) reminiscent of the sapient type. Also taking into account the finds on Mount Carmel, these scientists claim that the Ehringsdorf remains are relics of a hybrid population, produced by the mingling of Neanderthalers and early sapient forms of southern and south-eastern origin.

New discoveries will doubtless throw further light on the problem of the evolutionary place of Neanderthal Man, of whose importance there is no longer any doubt.

# LATER PALAEOLITHIC MAN

Beginning with the later Palaeolithic, i.e. the Aurignacian cultural period, human remains of a completely different physical type appear. They belong to higher racial types and are more finely modelled. The skull is characterised by a large, well-shaped cranium and a high, broad, prominent forehead. The face has lost its animal-like features, the jaws do not protrude like a snout and the chin is well-developed and juts out. The general posture is the same as in modern man, and the dimensions of the long bones of the limbs are the same.

From the Aurignacian period onwards, therefore, man's prehistoric evolution enters a new stage, with the appearance of a modern type of human being — *Homo sapiens fossilis,* or *diluvialis.* These individuals were much more widely distributed than the Neanderthalers and left considerable evidence of great economic, social and cultural progress.

## CRO-MAGNON MAN APPEARS ON THE SCENE

In 1886, the bones of five human beings — three males and probably one female and one child — were found in a cave in Cro-Magnon Rock at Les Eyzies, in the Dordogne, in France. These bones became famous because they provided science with one of the first examples of the later Palaeolithic Cro-Magnon race. The most famous is the skeleton of an old man, generally known as the 'old man of Cro-Magnon', which shows all the typical features of this race. Since then many others have been found in various countries.

In addition to the Cro-Magnon type, other bones, which show marked physical variations, have also been found. In the Grotte des Enfants cave, near Menton on the French Riviera, two skeletons were unearthed, at a depth of about 27 feet. They were of a young man and an old woman, both in crouching position. Both possessed physical characteristics similar to the features of the negro race. Some have therefore classified them as negroid, and by these they are regarded as members of the Grimaldi race, which may have found its way from Africa to the south of France at the beginning of the later Palaeolithic.

Another type was found in Chancelade in Southern France in 1886. This skeleton was of a male, and differed from both the afore-mentioned types. The members of this race were small, averaging under five feet in height. They had a very long, high head, with a long, wide face and prominent cheekbones. The orbit was large and square, and the bones of the hands relatively long and massive, indicating powerful muscle development. This skeleton, belonging to the Magdalenian cultural period, gave its name to the Chancelade race.

## THE LIFE OF LATER PALAEOLITHIC MAN

Later Palaeolithic Men were skilled hunters of great experience. Their weapons were superior to those of Neanderthal Man. They possessed good spears with sharp stone or bone tips, and later fashioned bows and arrows. They also had bolas, weighted at one end with stones or with spherical or cylindrical weights of mammoth ivory. They likewise used stone disks for hurling, and possessed sharp daggers made from the bones of animals.

41

They had also devised new ruses for hunting. They knew how to dig deep pits, which they dug along the routes to the animals' drinking pools, camouflaging them with branches and turf. Sometimes they drove the animals into the bogs and marshes, or brought them to bay in a cul-de-sac, where they killed them in large numbers. Their cave drawings also show that they constructed traps of different kinds.

Another trick was to disguise themselves in animals' skins and to crawl up to their quarry. Sometimes they needed no more than a handful of branches. When sufficiently close, advancing against the wind, they pounced upon and speared the startled beasts.

There is also evidence of large-scale hunting. One of the best finds was a rock near Solutré, north of Lyon. Prehistoric hunters apparently used this rock for hunting wild horses, since the underlying layer is full of their bones. The number of animals involved has been estimated at 100,000.

The largest known mammoth cemetery is in Předmostí, near Přerov, in Moravia (Czechoslovakia). Here the bones of at least 1,000 mammoths were found, all of which had been killed by Aurignacian hunters.

Later Palaeolithic hunters pursued every species in their neighbourhood. They probably avoided direct battle with the ferocious cave lion, however, though pursuing it by other methods. They hunted not only for meat but also for skins, with which they covered themselves, their tents and their huts. Bones, teeth and horns were used to make implements, weapons and ornaments. Magdalenian hunters specialised in making weapons for use against reindeer. They made bone spearheads with a groove to facilitate bleeding, toothed harpoons and special sticks from which they hurled their spears and javelins with greater speed and penetrating force.

Although hunting was the main occupation of these people, meat was not always plentiful. It had to be supplemented with vegetable food and this was probably the responsibility of children and old people. Although plants are rarely included in drawings and engravings, berries, roots and other plant foods probably found a prominent place in their diet.

Since they now lived, at least seasonally, in large communities, large quantities of food were required, and this resulted in frequent changes of habitat. In cold weather they must have gone hungry and sometimes starved. Even in summer there was unlikely to have been a super-abundance of food, since in warm weather the meat soon decayed and had to be consumed quickly. Conditions must have been greatly alleviated when it was found that meat could be dried and smoked. This was probably an accidental discovery, and although it was a great step forward, supplies still depended on the fortunes of the hunt, since Palaeolithic man had not yet learnt to domesticate animals and to keep them in herds.

The places where they lived are known as encampments, settlements or stations. During the cold glacial periods they lived in caves, and during the warmer intervals the encampments were erected under overhanging cliffs or in the open.

Cave settlements were always near the entrance, where it was lighter and less damp. At night the fires spread light and heat and kept wild beasts away. The caves had high, wide entrances and a large, spacious 'hall'. They provided shelter from rain, wind and snow but could not keep out the cold. It is possible, therefore, that primitive tent-like structures were set up within the caves as added protection.

When they camped in the open they set up hut-like or tent-like structures for protection against the elements. These were built of strong branches, covered with animal skins. They were no doubt light and portable, easy to take down and to rebuild.

Recent investigations in the steppes of the Ukraine show that, as an additional protection, they sometimes dug trenches, divided into sections, each with its own fire. The trench was covered with a tent-like roof, consisting of a framework of stakes, probably covered on top with skin and birch bark, and on the sides with clay and mammoth tusks.

The Magdalenian hunters who occupied what is now the Ukraine were also most ingenious. As seen from Gorodtsov's excavations on Timonovka, they lived in right-angled trenches, the walls of which were lined with wood and the roof composed of beams about eight inches thick. The roof was covered with earth, and as this was soon overgrown with grass, the trench was indistinguishable from the surrounding steppe. The trench was entered by a sloping passage about three feet wide, also roofed over. It is interesting to note that for each dwelling trench there were several conical pits serving as food stores.

Soviet research workers also found traces of later Palaeolithic dwellings in the far north. In Buret they found four buildings composed of bones of the mammoth and hairy rhinoceros. Even the columns supporting the roof were made not from tree trunks but from long mammoth shin bones or tusks. The walls and foundations were made from rhinoceros skulls and other large bones, interspersed with slabs of stone and clay. The roof was also of bones, including those of reindeer.

These people always knew the best sites for their settlements. They built them mainly on southern slopes, protected where possible by rocks or hills against the north wind. They always settled near water, and if near a river, well out of the way of possible floods. The fact that animals came to the water to drink also made hunting easier. In the selection of a site attention was probably paid not only to the movements of herds of animals but also to those of unfriendly tribes.

All encampments were not of equal importance. Those which display poverty of the cultural layer indicate that they were used only for a short time. Others show rich cultural layers and were probably inhabited for long periods.

Life in the encampment centred around the fire. Here the hunters brought their game, and here it was eaten. It was beside the fire that the tribe rested, worked, played and held council. Large stones are often found round the fire, and they probably served as seats. Sometimes 'workshops' have been found near the fire, where the weapons and implements were made. These included many small objects for domestic use as well, bone clasps to fasten the clothes, bone needles and awls, primitive whistles and flutes, and small works of art, such as bracelets and necklaces. It was here that the skins of animals were treated and the clothing made, probably by the women and girls.

Little is known of their clothing habits. Although figures and pictures of men and women usually show them nude, clothing of a sort must have been worn. In summer they would need no more than a piece of skin round the hips and shoulders, but in winter they must have been completely wrapped in furs. The needles found in many encampments are sufficient evidence that they knew how to sew skins together into some forms of jackets and trousers, the former being fastened with special clasps. Some finds indicate that they decorated their clothes. In the grave of two children in the Grotte des Enfants near Menton, over one thousand small shells, with holes bored in them, were found in the pelvic area, where they had once either been sewn on the clothing or possibly strung as bead aprons. On the skull of the young man found in the same cave were four rows of snail shells, again bored with holes, which had once apparently embellished the head covering.

A recent Soviet find provides further information. In Buret a female figurine was discovered, differing from others by the fact that it was clothed. The northern type of clothing depicted consists of a kind of one-piece fur suit (not opening down the front), with a hood. It would seem to have been excellently adapted for arctic conditions.

Late Palaeolithic hunters adorned their bodies as well as their clothing. They wore necklaces and bracelets, and some statuettes show that the women often wore their hair carefully dressed in complicated styles.

The encampment fires were maintained chiefly by the wood of local trees, but the bones of large animals were also used. In Věstonice in Czechoslovakia, a semi-circular group of long mammoth bones was found round the remains of a fire, the broken ends pointing inwards towards the centre of the fire. It was evidently kept alight by the fat from the ends of the bones. Another remarkable find recently made in Czechoslovakia was that of a Palaeolithic station near Ostrava, where the fire already appeared to have been maintained with bituminous coal obtained from a seam leading up to the surface.

## BURIAL CUSTOMS

Many Aurignacian burials have been found. As a rule, the dead were buried in the encampment itself. Some tribes dug graves, often encasing the head and feet in stones; others weighted down the head, chest and feet with stones as if to ensure that the dead man should not rise. Some corpses were bound hand and foot, in a crouching position. Sometimes the dead were left in the cave and the entrance blocked by a boulder. Various gifts were placed in the graves, including ornaments, stone implements and food.

Unique among Aurignacian graves is that of the mammoth hunters discovered by K. J. Maška in 1894, in Předmostí, Czechoslovakia. It contained twenty skeletons, all buried in a crouching position and all facing north. Five were of adult men, three of adult women, two of girls, seven of children and three of babies. The grave was oval and was thirteen feet long and eight feet wide. One side was lined with mammoth shoulder blades and the other with mammoth jawbones. The grave was covered with a layer of limestone rocks twelve to twenty inches deep, to protect the grave against wild beasts. It appears to have been used for regular burial.

## THE DAWN OF ART

If we wish to seek for the beginnings of art we must go back far beyond the ancient Egyptians, Chaldeans or Babylonians to the Aurignacian and Magdalenian hunters who left the first works of art ever known. The most famous examples come from France and Spain. We owe our knowledge of Palaeolithic art to the French scholar, Professor H. Breuil.

Palaeolithic art budded during the beginning of the Aurignacian period and blossomed into full flower during the Magdalenian period. Animals and women formed the main subjects of this art. The first discovery was by Marcelino de Sautuola in the cave of Altamira. He declared that the splendid polychrome paintings adorning the walls of the cave were actually palaeolithic in origin, but it was some time before expert authorities accepted the fact.

Palaeolithic art may be classified in three groups; firstly, small portable objects decorated with painting, engraving or carving; secondly, figurines representing animals and people; thirdly, mural paintings and engravings in caves or on rocks.

The oldest works of art of the Aurignacian mammoth hunters include nude female figures, known as 'Venuses'. The face, hands and feet of these figures are usually neglected, while the breasts, belly and thighs are exaggerated. These figurines are generally carved from mammoth tusks or bones, though some are made either of sandstone or a substance composed of burnt bones, clay and tallow. Today there are a large number of Venuses of varying provenance; they range in size from two to four inches, sometimes as much as five or six. All are nude, with the exception of the Buret figurine. They were clearly not fashioned according to the prevailing ideas of feminine beauty, and are therefore likely to be relics of some ancient fertility cult.

Male figurines, emphasising their masculinity, are much rarer. One such figure, carved from mammoth ivory, was found in a grave near Brno, Czechoslovakia. Animal figures are also known, some of them exquisitely formed.

More common than figurines, however, are engravings, both simple and ornamental. Most of these depict animals, some very amateurish, others more masterly. All show that the artists were perfectly familiar with the characteristics of the animals concerned. They are carved in ivory, deer-antler, bone, stone, stalagmite and stalactite and on cave walls, and show animals in typical poses or in motion, often wounded or dying.

The only instrument employed was the flint graver. Despite its simplicity, however, the best work has surprising beauty and artistic value, especially where the artist made ingenious use of the unevenness of the cave wall in his engravings.

Palaeolithic art culminates, however, in the wonderful animal paintings which decorate some caves in France and Spain. These are the most valuable and admired relics of this branch of prehistoric art. The most famous are those of Altamira in Spain, and of Font-de-Gaume, Les Combarelles and Lascaux in France. The artists used coloured minerals, particularly yellow ochre and red iron ore, in shades ranging from brown to red. They mixed their colours with animal fat and applied them either with their fingers, or possibly with wooden or bone sticks. They may have used primitive brushes as well, made from pieces of hairy hide. For palettes they used the shoulder blades of animals they had killed.

It is no longer thought that the Palaeolithic hunter-artist depicted animals for his pleasure or to decorate his cave home. The animals were drawn as objects of his hunting. It was an attempt in some way to influence the course and outcome of the hunt, on which their lives depended. The pictures, therefore, primarily formed a part of their hunting-magic cult. There is considerable evidence to support this view. The drawings and paintings are always at some distance from the cave mouth and in many cases in hidden, inaccessible recesses. They are also in complete darkness, where the only illumination could have come from the torches of the cave dwellers who came for a specific purpose. The connection of these pictures with a hunting-magic cult is also seen from engravings and paintings in which the animals' bodies are pierced with arrows and spears. In some pictures, actual arrows were used, while in others the animals are drawn in association with various structures thought to be traps.

Many such recesses are so richly decorated that they may be regarded as prehistoric temples, in which various magic rites, based on superstition, were performed. One such sanctuary was discovered in the Haute-Garonne department of France, another in the Tuc d'Audoubert cave on the southern side of the Pyrenees. In the latter a statue was discovered, about three feet high, depicting two bisons, male and female, about to mate. The figures were made of clay, and the footprints of the people who danced around the statue could still be seen. The rites performed here were clearly connected with human fertility, and since the footprints are those of young people, it may be assumed that initiation ceremonies to adulthood were performed.

In addition to ceremonial objects, dancing, singing and masks, magic rites require a sorcerer. There are in fact pictures of sorcerers, that of the Trois Fréres cave in the Pyrenees being the best known. Apart from pictures of sorcerers there are also drawings of people wearing masks, and representations of beings part human and part animal. In Altamira, human figures with animal heads shaped into strange beaks were found, and similar monsters are depicted in caves in France. All this evidence goes to show that sorcery is the earliest form of religion, and sorcerers the first priests.

# LIST OF PLATES

PLATES

# AUSTRALOPITHECINAE

South African Australopithecinae, one of man's animal ancestors, inhabited grassy plains without spreading forests. They were no longer the anthropoid apes of the primaeval forests, but creatures of the steppe. They walked erect, or almost erect. We do not know whether they actually made their homes in caves and clefts in the limestone rocks, but they undoubtedly sought shelter there in time of need and danger. They differed from all anthropoid apes before and since by being predominantly meat-eaters. They hunted different types of game, including antelopes and baboons, and banded together when hunting to ensure greater success.

With the regression of certain animal characteristics important and advantageous for hunting (e.g. a decrease in the size of the teeth), the Australopithecinae began to arm themselves with various convenient implements, such as knotted sticks, sharp stones, antelopes' horns, the long bones of animals and similar objects. Their most dangerous weapons included the shoulder blades of certain hoofed animals, such as horses and giraffes, which they also hunted. None of these, however, can be regarded as properly produced weapons. They were probably the remains of bones cracked open by the Australopithecinae to obtain the marrow, which, because of their shape and size, were found suitable for killing or stunning. The latest reports, however, claim that at least some Australopithecinae produced some form of very simple, roughly fashioned stone implements.

We do not know how the Australopithecinae hunted their prey. From fractures in the skulls of some of the animals which they killed Professor Dart assumes that they were killed with stones hurled from some distance or height. This was obviously not the only method, however.

From finds of Australopithecine skulls (belonging to *Plesianthropus*), it can be deduced that their owners died a violent death; this is also sometimes regarded as evidence that some Australopithecinae, if not all, were cannibals.

The Australopithecinae probably lived during the Early and Middle Pleistocene, i.e. 900,000 to 500,000 years ago.

PLATE I

# PITHECANTHROPUS I

In the broad regions round the river Solo on the island of Java, in the shadow of big volcanoes, lived bands of the most primitive human beings, or Prehominids, whose first and best-known example is *Pithecanthropus erectus*, discovered near Trinil in the 1890's by Professor E. Dubois. With his bent head, coarsely modelled face with its small, broad nose and protruding, snout-like jaws, receding forehead, and thick supraorbital arches jutting out over the eyes like a roof, *Pithecanthropus* still resembled anthropoid apes in many respects.

*Pithecanthropus* probably roamed from place to place in small bands searching for food. They fed most likely on the juicy fruit of tropical trees and shrubs and dug up pulpy bulbs and sweet roots; on occasion they hunted small animals and plundered birds' nests. It is even possible that they did not despise carrion as long as it was not in too great a state of putrefaction.

They led simple lives, but they were always at war with nature. They were already, however, better equipped for battle than animals. They had legs on which they could walk and stand erect. As a result they held their heads better, they could focus better and their limbs increased in length. None of these changes had such a decisive or important influence on their general progress, however, as the development of their hands, which were now liberated for other work than merely walking. Their hands were their chief weapon in the struggle for existence. It was with their hands and their primitive intelligence that they set out to conquer the world. Together with other types of Prehominids, *Pithecanthropus* is the first representative of the oldest forms of human culture, which stretch back to the very beginning of the Early Palaeolithic. They mark the true beginning of man's early history and of his physical, mental and cultural progress.

PLATE 2

# PITHECANTHROPUS

The hand of *Pithecanthropus* was perhaps the first to fashion the most primitive stone implements. These implements were not actually found together with the bones of *Pithecanthropus*, but they were discovered on Java, in the same geological layers as the bones of *Pithecanthropus*.

The most important of these discoveries was made by Professor von Koenigswald near Krikilan, not far from Sangiran. These implements are small and were made from stone fragments. One side is smooth, while the other shows traces of having been treated. They are quite irregular in form. Almost all are primitive scrapers, with an occasional more delicately fashioned point or drill. They are yellowish or brown in colour, but all have a handsome patina.

There is no doubt that *Pithecanthropus* also used some kind of weapons. Besides pointed stones he probably used sharply pointed broken branches or clubs. These have not been preserved, as wood soon decays, but it can safely be assumed that they used them, since they were bound to discover their possibilities very early on. It would be sufficient, when fleeing from danger, to run up against the sharp stump of a broken branch. The torn and bleeding side or leg, together with the memory of the incident, would finally bring the realisation that a pointed broken branch would also be a good weapon and defence against enemies.

Stone implements and the primitive wooden spear were important inventions. They meant that *Pithecanthropus* was already capable of constructive thought.

This species did not make their home in caves, as the tropical climate in which they lived made this unnecessary.

PLATE 3

# HEAD OF PITHECANTHROPUS

The head of *Pithecanthropus*, as already mentioned, possessed many characteristic features reminiscent of the anthropoid apes.

On comparing the skull of *Pithecanthropus* with a modern, human skull, we see that it is smaller. On comparing it with the skull of the anthropoid apes, however, we see that it is larger. To someone who has seen the skull of an adult male gorilla, for example, this statement may seem strange. The size of the skull of anthropoid apes is delusive, however, since large bony crests, to which muscles are attached, are present on the vault. The skull of *Pithecanthropus* has no such crests — that is why it appears small — but the volume of the cranium is greater. It is this which is important for the size of the brain. A study of cranial capacity shows that in anthropoid apes it is 400 to 600 cc., in *Pithecanthropus* 800 to 1,000 cc. Although the cranial capacity of *Pithecanthropus* is still far from that of modern man, which averages about 1,420 cc., it nevertheless excludes *Pithecanthropus* from the anthropoid apes. Since the weight of the brain can also be determined from cranial capacity, it has been estimated that the brain of *Pithecanthropus* weighed about 750 grammes, while that of a gorilla weighs only 450 grammes and the average weight of the brain of modern man is about 1,350 grammes.

A number of research workers have studied the form and development of the brain of *Pithecanthropus* from cranial casts. The results show that it was basically an enlarged, highly perfected, anthropoid ape brain. Its most important feature is enlargement and development of the frontal lobes, which are the seat of higher mental activity. As compared with the brain of anthropoid apes this was undoubtedly an advantage and an evolutionary advance. The greater size of the left frontal lobe indicates that the right hand was more active and skilful than the left and that *Pithecanthropus* was right-handed, like modern man.

Enlargement of the frontal lobes was not the only evolutionary advance in the brain of *Pithecanthropus*. The visual and auditory centres in the occipital and temporal lobes also developed. *Pithecanthropus* thus had greater powers of observation than animals, he was better able to understand what he saw and by his vision he directed his primitive work. He was also able to understand and differentiate sounds better. That was not all, however. He also attempted to imitate sounds, or even to form new sounds, in an effort to make himself understood. With *Pithecanthropus* (and *Sinanthropus*) came the dawn of human speech, however simple and primitive its beginnings may have been. This is confirmed by the brain of *Pithecanthropus*, since in the lower part of the left frontal lobe can be seen the faint outline of a convolution which in modern man is very marked and which contains the motor speech centre (known as Broca's centre). *Pithecanthropus* was not alalic, i.e. incapable of speech, as supposed by Professor Ernst Haeckel, although his capacity for speech and the structure of his speech were naturally extremely primitive.

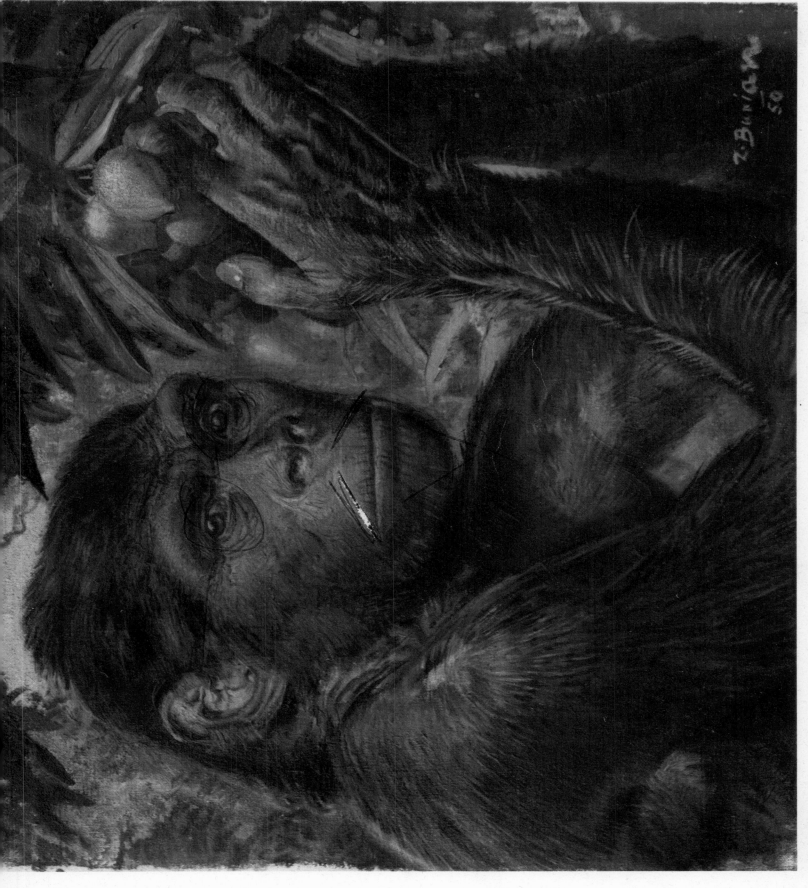

PLATE 4

# PITHECANTHROPUS AND NATURE

*Pithecanthropus* lived in small groups in natural surroundings full of difficulties and dangers. It was this constant struggle with nature which helped these beings to develop their primitive minds and to perfect their senses, which they now began to use in a human manner.

*Pithecanthropus* was well acquainted with nature. It was not so long ago that he himself emerged from the animal kingdom and he still possessed many animal instincts. He was already aware, however, that brute force would not get him very far. On the contrary, with brute force he would be at a disadvantage against his animal ancestors. Not only was he weaker, he was also defenceless, since he had lost the powerful teeth and sharp canines of his ape forbears. His mind, however, primitive though it was, made him superior to all other living creatures. His hands, though still clumsy, formed the first stone instruments and heavy clubs or sharp spears. With his stone implements he could dig up fleshy roots or cut up his prey, and he defended himself with clubs and spears.

There were many dangers, however, against which *Pithecanthropus* was still powerless. Of course there were the volcanoes, whose frequent eruptions brought panic and death. Even more important were the beasts of prey, from which his life was constantly in danger. The most terrible of these was the sabre-toothed tiger (*Epimachairodus zwierzycki*), of the Early and Middle Pleistocene, whose upper canines were long and curved like sabres, with a flattened back edge sharp as a knife. There is no doubt that the sabre-toothed tiger often struck terror into the heart of these creatures.

It is not known whether *Pithecanthropus* knew and used fire, even if he himself was still unable to make fire, since no traces of evidence have been found. It is not absolutely out of the question, however, since he would have been able to obtain fire from volcanic eruptions. Other Prehominids (the Chinese *Sinanthropus*) knew fire and even knew how to use it to their own advantage.

PLATE 5

# HOW FIRE WAS OBTAINED

Chinese Prehominids — the *Sinanthropus* of Choukoutien (*Sinanthropus pekinensis*), who are an extremely important link in knowledge of man's forebears in general, were already acquainted with fire. The discovery of the remains of their fires came as a surprise.

It is thought that they were unable to make fire themselves and that they obtained it by chance, possibly when the lightning set fire to the dry grass of the steppe and the fire spread to shrubs and small woods. *Sinanthropus* no doubt feared fire at first, running away from it and hiding in caves. When the fire was already spent, however, when the flames no longer shot up high into the air and the unbearable heat had died down, some of the boldest probably ventured close to the flames. No doubt they inspected the embers inquisitively, poking them, and jumped up in alarm at the shower of hot sparks which flew up. One of them possibly threw a handful of dry grass or twigs on to the embers and when they burst into flames, they realised how a fire had to be fed in order to keep it alive. We do not know how they transported the embers to their caves; they may have carried them in a hollow bone, or have taken back a thick branch still burning at one end. It is certain, however, that they had fires in their caves and that these were carefully tended for many generations, as seen from the layers of ash more than twenty feet deep.

The possession and utilisation of fire was of the greatest importance for *Sinanthropus*. The wild beasts feared the fire and gave a wide berth to a cave where a fire was burning. The light of the fire also put to flight the terrors of the darkness. The fire provided warmth, and meat thrown into the flames and embers had a better flavour. This latter discovery was probably made outside the cave. When *Sinanthropus* went out into the steppe after a big fire, he no doubt found the bodies of many dead animals, whose half-roasted flesh had a pleasant flavour. Later, therefore, he roasted his catch himself, not only because of the flavour, but also because roasting made the meat more tender. Lastly, it was fire which made it possible for *Sinanthropus* to live for so many generations in this region, with its not very favourable climatic conditions.

In those faraway ages, fire was already man's protector and friend.

PLATE 6

# HEIDELBERG MAN

About 500,000 years ago, the Neckar flowed through the region between the Swabian Jura and the Rhine, flooding wide areas. At the beginning of the Quaternary the river beds were not deep and in flat country the rivers frequently changed their course, leaving sand and gravel alluvium behind.

At that time the Neckar country was enjoying the mild climate of the first (Günz-Mindel) interglacial period, or according to other datings, the warm interstadial of the second (Mindel) glacial period of the Ice Age. The countryside was overgrown with woods and dense shrubs, frequented by herds of the fossil forest elephant (*Elephas* or *Palaeoloxodon antiquus*) and the fossil rhinoceros (*Dicerorhinus etruscus*). Wild horses (*Equus mosbachensis*) galloped over the shrub-grown grasslands, herds of wild pigs (*Sus scrofa*) wallowed in the marshes and proudly-antlered elks (*Alces latifrons*) roamed about. In the water the giant beaver (Trogontherium) built dams. In the forests and thickets were the lairs of various beasts of prey, such as the bear (*Ursus deningeri*), various species of hyaena and the sabre-toothed tiger.

Through this country roamed small bands of the only European pre-human being who had existed hitherto — *Homo heidelbergensis* — whose lower jaw was found in October 1907, in a sandpit near the village of Mauer not far from Heidelberg in Germany. It is a large, massive jaw without a chin. The body is powerful and the rami carrying the articular surfaces are short and wide. The teeth have many human features, although they are larger than those of modern man; one of the characteristic human signs is that the third molar, or 'wisdom' tooth, is small. In the development of the teeth, Heidelberg man was more advanced than the Javan *Pithecanthropus*, but in the structure of the jaw the reverse applies.

This species roamed about in small bands, hunting small or medium-sized game and gathering fruit or roots. The game was cut up by means of primitive stone implements, which were not discovered until 1956, when they were found by Alfred Rust in the same layer as that in which the Mauer jaw had been found. These implements were sharpened at the edges. They were all made from local material (siliceous sandstone). The commonest type was an implement shaped like a plane. According to Rust, the almost complete absence of hand stones is evidence of the antiquity and independence of this Early Palaeolithic culture and it has therefore been termed the Heidelberg phase.

PLATE 7

# THE NEANDERTHAL ENCAMPMENT

During the Early Palaeolithic, wide areas of the Old World were lived over by the Neanderthalers, the first true human beings to appear on the earth. They made their homes in caves or under jutting rocks. When the climate permitted, they also camped in the open.

They always lived in small communities, meeting the hardships of their life together. They were small in stature but robustly built, with a broad, rather than a long, chest. They were strong, as seen from the large muscle-insertions on their bones — evidence of powerful development. Their legs were relatively short and bent at the knees. Their structure and the appearance of the spine make it possible to form an idea of the Neanderthalers' gait. They walked with a shuffle because their feet still did not possess the arch which gives modern man his soft and springy step. The bones of the legs also show another interesting feature. The tibia and fibula have special small arricular surfaces, indicating that the Neanderthalers had the habit of sitting on their haunches, as children and many primitive tribes still do today. The whole of the upper half of the body leaned forward, as if dragged down by the heavy head. Balance was maintained by slight bending at the knees. The hand of Neanderthal man was well developed and heavy, like the hands of all who require great strength for their work. According to the Soviet scientist Bonch-Osmolovsky, however, it was not capable of delicate movements. He bases this view on the fact that the thumb joint is formed differently from that of modern man.

The community kept strictly together. They hunted together and shared the spoils. Apart from a few objects of personal interest, private property was unknown. Natural division of labour appears to have been practised in Neanderthal communities. While the men were concerned mainly with hunting and quartering the spoils, the women probably treated the skins, gathered fruit and roots, collected wood for maintaining the fire, and so forth.

The Neanderthalers did not adorn themselves with any ornaments and left no cultural relics to posterity.

PLATE 8

# WHAT THE NEANDERTHALERS LOOKED LIKE

Today we have a good idea of what Neanderthal man looked like. The many bones which have been found have made it possible to reconstruct his probable likeness and to determine in what respects he differed from modern man, though of course much of our idea of his external appearance must remain pure guesswork.

The most striking differences are in the skull. The skull of the Neanderthaler is usually large, with a low, flat, receding forehead and powerful supraorbital ridges, jutting out over the large orbits like a roof. The cranium is long and low with thick, massive bones. The root of the nose is broad. A glance at the profile draws attention to the protruding jaw, the resemblance of which to an animal's snout is enhanced by the absence of a chin. The low cranium, the flat forehead, the thick supraorbital ridges and the chinless lower jaw are the most important features reminiscent of the anthropoid apes.

From the skeletal findings it is safe to say that Neanderthal man was no Adonis — judging by our own standards of good looks. His face was large, broad and long. His snout-like jaws with their powerful teeth were topped by a broad, low, but prominent nose. His thick supraorbital ridges were probably overgrown with bushy eyebrows overhanging deep and wide-set eyes. His flat forehead receded into a low cranium, which merged at the back with his powerful neck. Thick hair grew on the top of his head and down the nape of his neck. The neck itself was short. The whole body inclined slightly forwards. The average height was about 160 cm. (5 ft. 3 in.) for men and 155 cm. (5 ft. 1 in.) for women.

These characteristics, which are typical chiefly for West European Neanderthal man of the beginning of the last (Würm) glacial period, were somewhat more refined in women and children. In some of the earlier (Last Interglacial) Neanderthalers certain differences occurred, including vaulting of the forehead and incipient signs of a chin.

PLATE 9

# WINTER HARDSHIPS

The later Neanderthalers did not have an easy life. They inhabited no Garden of Eden, but were constantly in difficulties and constantly at war with nature. During the summer, life was easier; in the winter and during cold and rainy periods it was worse. It is likely that they had to protect themselves from the cold and frost by coarsely fashioned skins, in which they wrapped themselves from head to foot; that they slept on skins, lying down to rest on piles of dry grass and moss; and that mothers wrapped their infants in skins. More fires appear to have been lit in the caves in those days, round which all the members of the community crouched to warm themselves. It is also possible that some kind of curtain of skins was hung at the entrance to the cave to keep out cold winds and frosts. Whether the winter was passed in relative comfort undoubtedly depended on the number of skins, which in turn depended on the fortune of the hunt.

During the winter, want and hunger were frequent guests. Hunting was difficult and the hunters often returned empty-handed. When they succeeded, however, in catching a large animal, such as a wild boar, the meat naturally kept longer than in the summer, when the heat soon caused it to putrefy. We do not know whether the Neanderthalers knew anything about keeping food, but it seems as though in times of plenty they gorged themselves, without any thought for the future.

Because of their hard conditions of life, the Neanderthalers did not live to a ripe old age. From certain infallible signs in their bones and teeth we know that they died relatively very young. The oldest examples known are those from La Chapelle aux Saints and the Neanderthal itself. The former of these (a man) died at about forty, the latter (also a man) between forty and fifty. The inclement climate, hunger, disease, constant danger, insufficient hygiene and care, all combined to bring about the early death of people who otherwise were strong and resistant. It is interesting to note the distribution of mortality according to sex. During the whole of the Stone Age, most of those who survived the age of thirty were men; up to that age mortality was highest among women. This is no doubt related to child-bearing; in serious cases, lack of hygiene and proper help must have caused the death of many a young Neanderthal mother.

PLATE 10

# BURNING THE POINTS OF THE SPEARS

Most of Neanderthal man's surviving implements and weapons were made of stone. In his hand, the rough hand-axe acquired an almond-like or triangular form. One of their most important instruments was a kind of stripper, in which only one of the long edges was sharpened. This was used mainly for treating skins. Short, broad flakes of stone were used to make knives, spear points, primitive drills and other necessary implements.

The Neanderthalers made most of their instruments from flint, because it was easy to chip and because of the sharpness of the flakes. In France flint was plentiful and there it was most frequently used. In regions where no flint was available the situation was more difficult. If there was no moraine in the vicinity, which carried flint from the Baltic, the Neanderthalers had to be content with other stones. These implements were rougher, however, and never so perfect as flint instruments.

Occasionally the Neanderthalers used as weapons fragments of the long bones of their prey (usually the cave bear). The lower jaw of the bear, with its powerful canines, made a dangerous life-preserver.

PLATE II

# HUNTING THE CAVE BEAR

The Neanderthalers were already such mighty hunters that they knew how to hunt big animals. In Europe, they were fond of hunting the cave bear. Amazing quantities of cave bear bones are found in their encampments — so many, in fact, that some of the Neanderthalers ought to be known as 'cave bear hunters'. The commonest way in which they hunted the bears was probably by lying in wait on the sheer cliffs above the entrance to the cave, or in narrow clefts in the rocks. When the bears appeared, they would hurl down boulders on them, usually with some success.

Big animals had to be hunted collectively. It is impossible to imagine collective hunting and community life in general without speech. There had to be some way of communicating ideas, knowledge and experience; there had to be some way of coming to an understanding over the hunt, some way of issuing directions. Community life made communication essential.

The question of whether Neanderthal man was able to speak is answered by a study of his brain. Casts of the cranial cavity show that the lower part of the left frontal lobe contained a clearly defined area which in modern man forms the speech centre. Insertions have also been found on the lower jaw, belonging to muscles controlling the movements of the tongue in the formation of individual sounds. The Neanderthalers were thus able to speak.

Their speech was no doubt very simple and abrupt, being probably composed only of simple words expressing given conceptions. These would develop not only from certain calls giving information on direction, place, distance, size, form, movement, number, etc., but also from hearing and imitating the noises made by animals (the mammoth, bear, wolf, birds, etc.), or the sounds of nature itself (the rustling of the trees, the cracking of wood, the babbling stream). These calls and sounds would in time become familiar to all and would eventually become the fixed expressions for given conceptions, thus becoming spoken words.

At first these words were few, but their number continuously increased and speech became richer in expressions and more intricate. In Neanderthal man it probably never reached a high level, but his simple, primitive language was a significant and decisive step forward in man's development, since speech is the first and most important foundation stone in the whole structure of human knowledge.

PLATE 12

# HUNTING IN THE DRAGON'S LAIR

A special form of bear-hunting was practised by the Neanderthalers who once lived near what is now Graz, in Austria.

High up in the limestone rock face above the bed of the river Mur, near the village of Mixnitz, is the dark entrance to the famous Drachenhöhle (Dragon's Lair), which is 500 metres (over 1,600 feet) long. At one time the cave was filled to a considerable height with different deposits rich in phosphate. During the First World War, when this phosphate earth was removed, it was subjected to detailed palaeontological and palaeoanthropological examination. Not only were quantities of bones of different Pleistocene animals found, but the cave also contained the remains of fires of Neanderthal hunters and stone and bone implements and weapons. Most of the bones were those of cave bears, indicating that the Dragon's Lair was long a favourite resort of these animals.

The Mixnitz Neanderthalers were the cave bear's greatest enemy. An encampment of Neanderthal hunters was found in the cave at the foot of a second landslide. The floor of this cave was paved with flat stones to protect the hunters from the damp as they sat round the blazing fire. This was not a permanent encampment, however, but was used only when hunting the cave bear. They startled the bears by fire and shouting, compelling them to flee through a narrow crack between the wall of the cave and the large boulders of the collapsed cave roof. Where the crack opened out into the broad cave, hunters armed with sticks, clubs and stone weapons waited for the bears as they sought to escape to safety from the cave. They probably avoided battle with old cave bears, which was difficult and dangerous, preferring to attack young animals, which were less dangerous and easier to overcome. When the hunt was over they returned to their usual haunts.

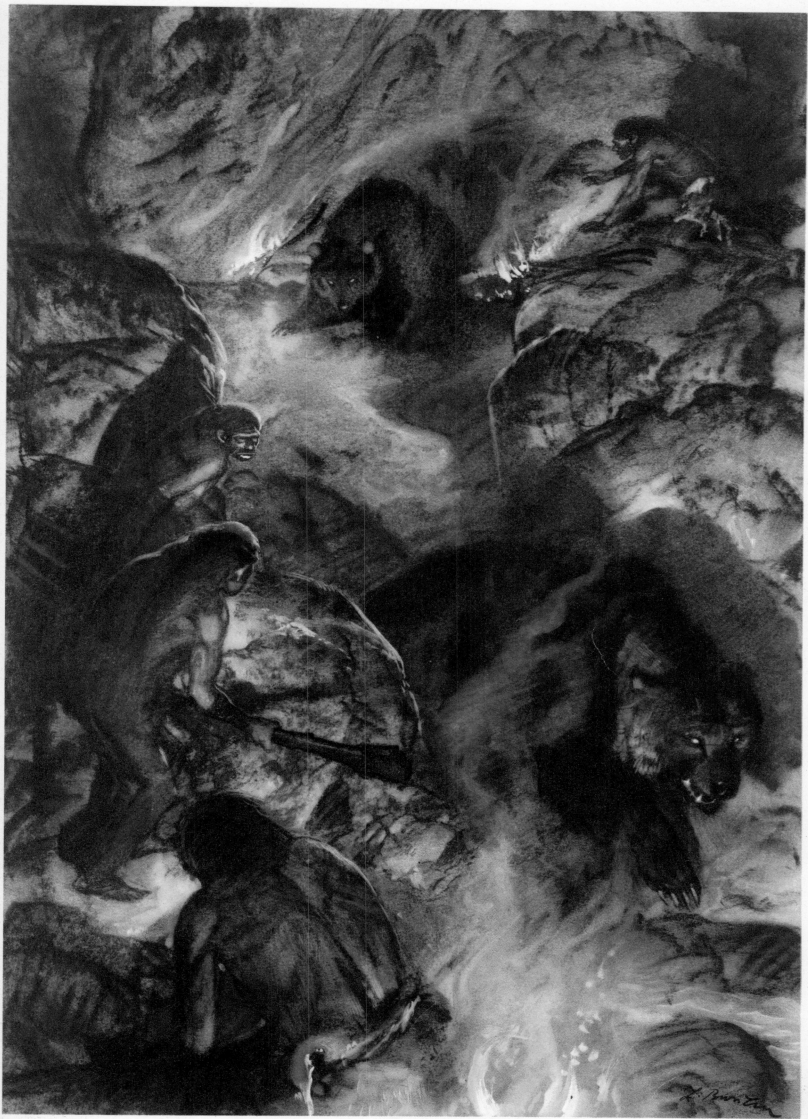

PLATE 13

# HUNTING THE SIBERIAN IBEX

The art of hunting big animals was one of the great achievements of the Neanderthalers, since it meant that they were in command of hunting artifices and stratagems.

The idea of using tricks when hunting developed among intelligent hunters who observed their surroundings and the habits of animals. A chance fall by some big animal into a natural ditch, such as a hollow tree blown down by the storm, might have given rise to the idea of digging an artificial pit on frequented trails and covering it with branches and earth to hide it.

The Neanderthal hunters who once inhabited the cave of Teshik-tash in Uzbekistan were no doubt acquainted with such hunting devices. They specialised in hunting the Siberian ibex *(Capra sibirica)*, an exceedingly timid and vigilant animal. To be able to catch it the Teshik-tash Neanderthalers must have been efficient, clever hunters, well acquainted with the habits of their prey and able to make use of their knowledge of the terrain. They appear to have driven the ibexes on to the rocks separated from the others by deep, narrow clefts, over which only the biggest and strongest could leap to safety. Those which failed fell to the bottom of the cleft, where they lay with broken limbs, an easy prey for the hunters. They were then carried back to the cave and eaten.

PLATE 14

# HUNTING THE HAIRY RHINOCEROS

In addition to implements and weapons, large numbers of animal bones are also found in Neanderthal encampments. These remains of their prey show what kind of animals they hunted and ate and which kinds were most frequently on the menu. As already mentioned, the commonest in Europe was the cave bear, while among the Teshik-tash Neanderthal hunters of Central Asia it was the Siberian ibex. These were not the biggest animals hunted by the Neanderthalers, however.

The Neanderthalers who lived after the peak of the last (Riss-Würm) interglacial period near what is now Taubach near Weimar, in Germany, actually hunted such enormous animals as the fossil elephant *Elephas (Palaeoloxodon) antiquus* or the fossil rhinoceros *Coelodonta merckii* (or *Dicerorhinus kirchbergensis*). The remains of the fire of the encampment found here contained broken and partly burnt bones of these great animals, which could not be hunted without experience, cunning and inventiveness. The elephant or rhinoceros would first be cut up on the spot and then carried back to the camp fire where it was roasted and eaten. The long bones were cracked open to extract the marrow. The bones found at Taubach were chiefly those of young animals. This indicates that primarily young animals were hunted, probably because they were easier to catch and the hazards were less than with the hunting of old animals. Another possible reason is that young animals, being inexperienced, were more likely to fall into the different snares and traps.

The Neanderthalers living at the beginning of the last (Würms) glacial period also hunted the rhinoceros. This was no longer the warmth-loving, hairless fossil rhinoceros *Coelodonta merckii*, but the hairy *Coelodonta antiquitatis*, usually to be found with the mammoth. The hairy rhinoceros was also probably caught, as a rule, in artificial, camouflaged pits.

PLATE 15

# MOVING TO NEW HUNTING GROUNDS

Because of the way in which the Neanderthalers obtained their food, i.e. by gathering plants and by hunting, there came a time when the country round their encampment no longer provided them with enough to eat. Game was decimated or moved elsewhere. Places which once had been rich in roots and berries became impoverished. This entailed longer expeditions further and further afield and made conditions increasingly difficult both for hunting and for fruit and root-gathering. Want and hunger were constant problems. In the end the only solution was to strike camp and to move elsewhere.

This is what actually happened. The Neanderthalers often changed their encampment in their search for new sources of food. Since they always selected convenient sites, however, it often happened that years after, when the game was replenished and the plants had grown again, the tribe returned to an old haunt. They did not know that they had lived there before, since many generations had come and gone and the old encampment, together with the animals' bones and discarded or damaged implements and weapons (the 'cultural layer'), was covered with soil or some other deposit (the 'sterile layer'). Excavations in caves, for example, today suggest from the profile how often and for how long the cave was inhabited and how big was each population. Layers of later cultures are also sometimes found above layers of cultures of older races.

The tribe probably always moved as a whole, taking the most necessary articles (e.g. skins) with it. They moved together in one group, men, women and children. The Neanderthalers did not have families as we know them today; it should not be forgotten that they formed the most primitive type of human society.

PLATE 16

# WOUNDED BY A WILD BOAR

While the stone implements and weapons found in the encampments of the Neanderthalers tell us how they lived and worked, their bones tell us much about their illnesses and sufferings.

The most frequent danger in the lives of these people was wounding, when hunting or when fighting against an enemy. Pain often turned infuriated animals from the attacked into the attacker. In such cases, the hunter, while trying to escape, was often slightly or seriously wounded. The hunter seeking safety from a wounded bear by climbing a tree, for example, might not have been swift enough to escape with a whole skin, and the animal perhaps lacerated his leg with its mighty tusks. It is thought that the man from Neanderthal itself was severely wounded on a hunting expedition by a cave bear, which clawed through the skin of his arm and shoulder to the bone. The wound evidently healed comparatively well and rapidly, however, since only slight traces remained on the bone. The Broken Hill man in Rhodesia was less fortunate, since he suffered for a long time from a similar condition extending from the upper jaw to behind the ear; the crater-like pitting of the bones is a clear indication of a long suppurative process which refused to heal.

The Neanderthalers also suffered from severe toothache and often from suppurative processes, as seen from certain signs in many of their jaws. The Neanderthal man from La Chapelle aux Saints must have suffered excruciatingly; he lost all his teeth when young, his jaws rotted away from septic infection and although relatively young he looked like a toothless old man.

Rheumatism, caused primarily by the long periods spent in cold, damp caves, was a common scourge. Of the many examples it is sufficient to mention the poor creature of La Chapelle aux Saints, who also suffered from severe rheumatism, which involved the whole of the spine and several joints.

PLATE 17

# THE LE MOUSTIER BURIAL

One evening in March 1908, the Swiss prehistorian Otto Hauser, while carrying out research in the region of the river Vézère in France, received a pleasant surprise. One of his assistants working in Le Moustier came with the news that human bones had been found below an abri in a freshly uncovered cultural layer. Work had immediately been stopped so as not to damage the bones. The same night, in pouring rain, Hauser went to Le Moustier. When he had confirmed the truth of the report and the importance of the find, he decided to stop all work on the site and to continue only under the supervision of a commission of experts, so as to avoid any doubts and controversy over the age of the Le Moustier man.

The first commission met on April 18. It comprised only a few French doctors and officials. The purpose of this commission was simply to draw up a report on the finding and confirm it. The second commission — this time composed of actual experts — did not meet until August 9. Although Hauser sent out 600 invitations, only nine experts came, from Germany, headed by Professor Hermann Klaatsch, who had just been attending a congress of anthropologists in Frankfurt.

Although Professor Klaatsch did not at first believe the report that the find might be that of the skeleton of a Neanderthaler, he was soon convinced of his error when he began to uncover the skeleton. The skull, with its exceptionally well preserved teeth, was sufficient evidence in itself. This was not all, however. The experts found that this Neanderthal youth, who measured about 160 cm. (5 ft.), and was about 16 to 18 years old, had not just been thrown down, but had been buried. After his death, his fellows had dug a shallow grave; they laid him in it on his side, with his head resting on his right forearm and his left arm stretched forwards. They surrounded his head with large flint chippings and his body with stone instruments. They also placed meat in the grave, as seen from the animals' bones found there, many of which had been burnt when roasting the meat.

This rare find at Le Moustier did not remain in France. Hauser sold it, together with another, geologically younger skeleton from Combe Capelle, to Germany, for 160,000 marks. Failure of the bank in which he placed the money robbed him of three quarters of the sum. Hauser always retained a feeling of religious respect for his finds. Whenever he went to Berlin he always visited the museum and placed a bunch of red roses on the glass case in which they were kept. These skeletons are no longer in existence: they were destroyed during the Second World War.

PLATE 18

# THE BURIAL IN TESHIK-TASH

When Professor Alexei Pavlovich Okladnikov began his researches in the mountains of Baysun-tau in the valley of the river Surkhan, in June 1938, he chose as his base the village of Machai, from which he had received the majority of reports on finds of Palaeolithic stone instruments.

After a few days' investigations in some fifteen deep mountain valleys round Machai, the boys of the village took Okladnikov somewhere high up into the mountains. They first followed the bed of a mountain stream, but in a short time they began, slowly and carefully, to climb the rocks which gave the mountain-sides such a picturesque appearance. Narrow paths winding above sheer precipices finally brought them to a narrow rocky ravine, full of gravel washed down by the spring floods. Heedless of the gravel rolling under their feet and of the thorny briers, they entered the ravine and ploughed their way forwards. Suddenly, in a narrow bend of the ravine, Okladnikov saw the yawning entrance of a cave. As he looked at it he heard one of his guides remark 'Teshik-tash', which means 'the rock with a hole in it', i.e., a cave. Standing in front of this cave, which lay about 5,000 feet above sea level and measured 23 ft. x 66 ft. x 23 ft., Okladnikov could not dream that he was about to make one of the most important and famous discoveries of all time.

The finds made on the very first day convinced Okladnikov that more extensive and detailed investigations were necessary. The next day, therefore, he took with him twenty Machai farmers who were very interested in Okladnikov's work and had expressed their eagerness to help him. Okladnikov found that the cave contained five layers altogether, only two of which were cultural layers, indicating that the cave had twice been inhabited by Palaeolithic human beings. The most valuable finds were in the first cultural layer, which was full of stone weapons and the bones of animals which had been eaten.

It was not long, however, before Okladnikov made his great discovery, which made the obscure cave in Teshik-tash famous. Just after midday on July 4, 1938, Okladnikov found a human skull, which had disintegrated into many fragments, near the west wall. He soon recognised it as the skull of a Neanderthal boy aged about nine years. This was the first proof that Neanderthalers had lived in Central Asia. Further investigation showed that the boy had been buried, as his bones lay in a shallow grave. His head was surrounded by horns of the Siberian ibex (*Capra sibirica*), some whole, some broken. Two pairs were still firmly attached to fragments of the frontal bone, forming complete pairs. This also appears to have been the case with the other three or four pairs. One remarkable feature was that the horns had been thrust into the ground points downward, forming a kind of barrier round the boy's head. Not far from the grave were the remains of a small fire, which had burnt for a short time only. It may have been a ritual fire, connected with the burial, or it may have been part of an ibex cult, which still exists in Central Asia today, and which, according to Okladnikov, was already practised by the Neanderthalers of Teshik-tash.

# THE CULT OF THE BEAR

In 1917, when two Swiss research workers, Bächler and Nigg, began work in the Drachenloch (Dragon's Hole), their first finds of carefully arranged bones and skulls of cave bears (*Ursus spelaeus*) made them wonder whether they had found relics of some Neanderthal bear cult. Further excavations made them even surer that this was the case.

On August 23, 1920, when Bächler and Nigg began investigating the passage between the second and the third cave they found the remains of a fire surrounded by limestone boulders. Immediately beside it was a large stone cist, about three feet high, covered with a single limestone slab about five inches thick. Whey they opened the front, which was composed of 18 stones, the inside was found to be hollow, and after removing the covering slab, they were able to lift out seven splendidly preserved cave bear skulls, all of which had been placed there carefully, with their snouts pointing in the direction of the entrance. Two skulls still had the first two cervical vertebrae (the atlas and the axis) attached; in the others they were missing. Three tibiae, two ulnae and part of a humerus were propped against the side of the cist.

From this report of the finding of a stone grave for bear skulls it can be assumed, in agreement with Bächler and Nigg, that this was an ancient place of sacrifice. After a successful hunt, the Neanderthal hunters placed the bears' heads in the cist, probably together with certain rites. They did not necessarily fill the cist at once; it is more likely that the filling of the cist was the outcome of several hunts.

The peak of the Dragon Mountain, in which lies the Dragon's Cave, reaches high up into the clouds. To those who do not mind the effort and fatigue of the climb up its steep, rocky sides, it offers a magnificent view of the mountains around. It was not the beauty of the scenery which enticed the Neanderthal hunters up here, however. They came to hunt the cave bear and, if supposition is correct, after a successful hunt they carried out the rites of a mysterious hunting cult in the cave, by the light of pinewood flares.

PLATE 20

# THE CANNIBALS OF KRAPINA

The little town of Krapina, long famous in the scientific world, lies about two hours' journey to the north of Zagreb on the river Krapinica in the mountains between the Sáva and the Dráva. Long ago this little river hollowed out a small cave in the marine Miocene sandstone; actually it is not much more than an overhanging rock (an abri) which is now 80 feet above the bed of the river. At the beginning of the Pleistocene, the Krapinica flowed at the level of the floor of the cave, since the oldest layer is the gravel with which the Krapinica covered the floor of the cave. Later the river changed its course and ate deeper and deeper into the underlying rocks. The cave became dry and was filled with the products of weathering of the rocks to a height of 28 feet. The individual layers were obviously not deposited at once, so that at given times the cave housed different animals or Neanderthal human beings.

The most interesting of the nine layers were layers three and four, which contained over 300 fragments of human bones. Over 80 teeth, 50 skull fragments, 2 fragments of lower jaws, each with several teeth, the condyles of 6 lower jaws, 2 fragments of upper jaws, each with several teeth, broken ribs, fragments of long bones and shoulder blades and many frontal bone fragments with thick supraorbital arches were found. All these bones were mixed with ashes and charcoal. 'The whole of the third layer', declared Professor Gorjanovič-Kramberger, 'represents the remains of a single large fire, in which almost nothing but human skulls, all broken and scorched or burnt, was found. The bones belong to at least ten individuals of different ages (children and adults).'

Later research in the Krapina cave, in July 1905 (it was discovered and investigated for the first time in 1889) brought to light further remains of Neanderthalers, this time comprising over 200 fragments of bone. The bones, mixed with stone instruments and animal bones, lay directly on the site of the fire. An interesting find was that the long human bones, such as the humerus and femur, had been cracked open for their full length.

The human bones at Krapina were cracked and burnt. Their discoverers immediately assumed that they were probably the remains of cannibal feasts. The Krapina Neanderthalers thus not only hunted animals, but also hunted and killed their own kind. They roasted them at the camp fire, cracking open their long bones and skulls to extract the marrow and meat — a special delicacy.

No other such gruesome discoveries have been made in Europe, although indications of cannibalism have been found elsewhere. It is possible that some Neanderthal hunters held cannibalistic feasts at certain times or on particular occasions, or that they were sometimes driven to cannibalism by hunger. Cannibalism was definitely not a typical or general characteristic of Neanderthal man, however.

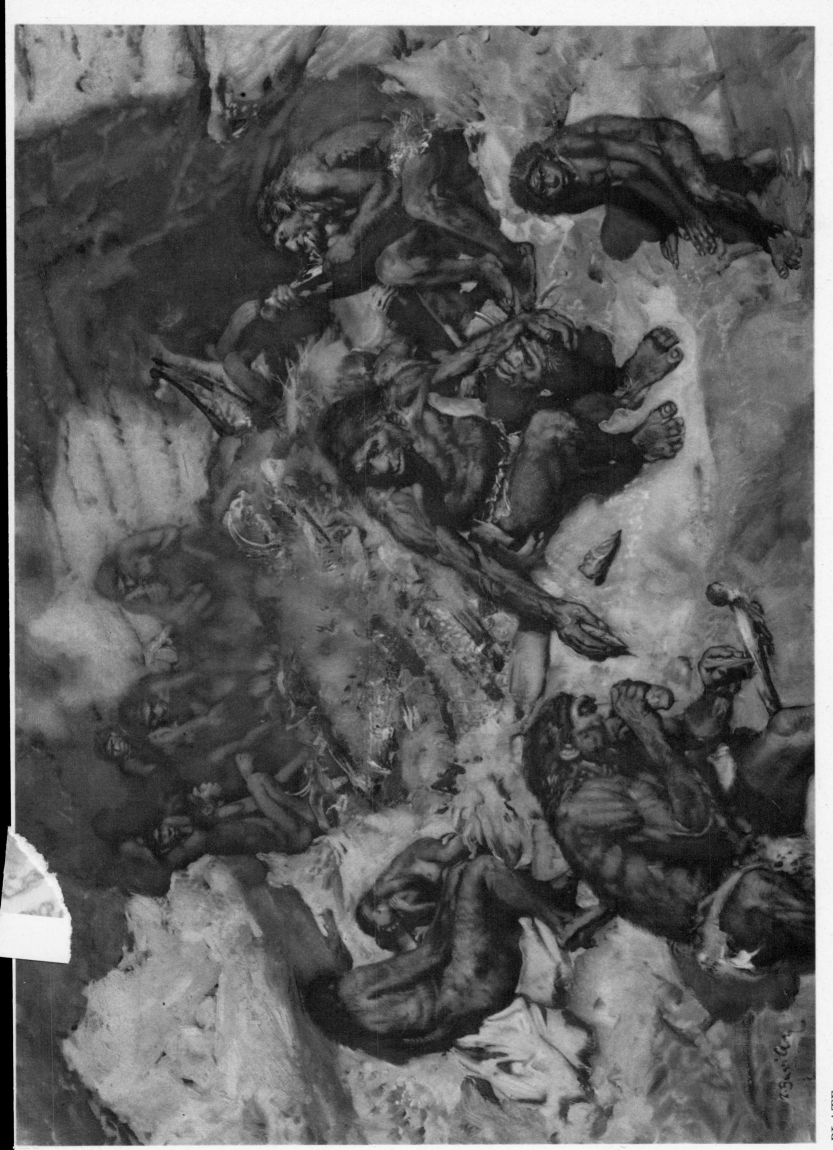

PLATE 21

# THE ENCAMPMENT IN NGANDONG

In 1931 and 1932, some very interesting discoveries were made near the village of Ngandong on Java. Eleven Neanderthal skulls were found in the highest terrace of the river Solo. In all the jaws were missing and in two the base of the skull had been shattered. Professor von Koenigswald concluded that they were relics of Javan Neanderthal head-hunters who had once camped here on the bend of the river Solo. This would only have been possible during the dry season, however. When the rains came they would have to leave immediately since the sand and gravel alluvium covered not only the bones of animals, which were scattered all around, but also the skulls of their dead enemies, which had possibly been impaled on a thick forked branch driven into the sand. The fleeing Neanderthalers vanished in the distance and their encampment, together with the bones of their prey and with their trophies, soon disappeared beneath the alluvium. Had it not been for the curiosity of modern man, they might still have been there today.

As distinct from European findings, the Javan finding is interesting because so many skulls were discovered in one place and all were in alluvial deposit. Professor von Koenigswald rightly points out that in the tropics, the climate was always such that the Neanderthal hunters were not obliged to shelter in caves, which — as the inhabitants of Java still believe today — are only the home of 'snakes, bats and evil spirits', (in the words of Professor von Koenigswald). That is why excavations in caves in the tropics never bear any results.

The fauna living at the time of the Ngandong Neanderthalers, which they hunted for food, differed from European fauna. The most common animals were the buffalo and the banteng (wild cattle still to be found in the jungles along the south coast of Java). Other common animals were deer (of the genera *Rusa* and *Axis*) and the wild boar. The hippopotamus basked in the waters of the river Solo, while the open country, which was not very thickly wooded, was the home of two species of elephants, one of which was related to the present Indian elephant, while the other was the last of the extinct genus *Stegodon*. Few remains of beasts of prey have been found, apart from a well preserved tiger's skull and a fragment of the jaw of a wild dog.

The Ngandong hunters lived at the same time as the European Neanderthalers at the beginning of the last glacial period. They lived under far more pleasant conditions, however, and probably displayed a characteristic which has not yet been found elsewhere, i.e. they were head-hunters.

PLATE 22

# ENCAMPMENT OF LATE PALAEOLITHIC HUNTERS

Neanderthal man (*Homo neanderthalensis*) died out at the end of the Middle Palaeolithic, about 70,000 years ago, and his fires were extinguished for ever. He was succeeded by a new, evolutionarily higher race, of the same type as modern man (*Homo sapiens*), which appeared in Europe and elsewhere during the Upper Palaeolithic. They are known as *Homo sapiens fossilis*, or *diluvialis*, to denote their greater geological age.

Late Palaeolithic man belongs to the First Interstadial (Würm 1-2) and later phases of the period. Many of his bony remains have been discovered, some in the open, some beneath overhanging rocks (abris) or in caves. The Aurignacian period began when he reached western Europe, the earliest and latest phases of which are known as the Early and Late Gravettian. In some of his encampments, particularly in the East, the waste from the cooking contains many mammoth bones. These hunters, who also differed from those of the West in certain minor features, are therefore known as mammoth hunters.

The stone weapons of these Aurignacian hunters are far more perfect than those of the Neanderthalers. From flint and chert they fashioned perfectly formed knives, burins, drills, scrapers, strippers and other instruments. Larger instruments were held in the hand, such as those used for skinning prey and for removing the meat from the bones. Smaller instruments were probably attached to wooden or bone handles. The blade-like forms of Aurignacian implements often have steeply-retouched backs ('backed blades'). The cultural progress of Aurignacian hunters was characterised not only by the production of more perfect stone implements and weapons, but also by an increase in the use of bone, from which they made daggers and spear points. They also began to make bone articles for domestic use, such as needles, clasps, etc. They were the first people to build dwellings and they were the first artists. They were likewise mighty hunters, the first to practise large-scale hunting.

PLATE 23

# A CRO-MAGNON HUNTER

In 1886, when the railway was being built in the valley of the river Vézère in France, five Late Palaeo-lithic skeletons were found in a cave near Cro-Magnon. The most famous is that of a man, which was nicknamed the 'old man of Cro-Magnon'. This skeleton attracted the attention of the experts and became the model and criterion of the 'Cro-Magnon race', then in its prime.

What did the 'old man of Cro-Magnon' look like? He was about six feet tall and robustly built. The muscle insertions on the skeleton show that he must have had very powerful muscles — a great advantage in the life of a Cro-Magnon hunter. His skull was long and large (cranial capacity 1,590 c.c.) and well vaulted; only the back was somewhat flattened. His forehead was high and the supraorbital ridges were only slightly thickened. His face was relatively low and broad, particularly over the cheekbones. His nose was long and narrow and the lower jaw had a good chin.

Apart from the Cro-Magnon race, which was very widespread and covered certain variable character-istics, there were several other Late Palaeolithic races, including the Grimaldi race, which was supposedly characterised by negroid features, and the Chancelade race.

PLATE 24

# A MAGDALENIAN HUNTER

At the beginning of the Magdalenian cultural period, which marked the end of the Upper Palaeolithic, the climate was still very cold. The last (Würm) glacial period was already past its peak, however, and towards the end of the Magdalenian period the climate was much milder and the gradual transition to the postglacial period had begun. At this time the mammoth and the hairy rhinoceros disappeared from South and Central Europe, moving north in the wake of the retreating ice sheet. The cave bear and the cave hyaena likewise disappeared. The wild horses, once so abundant, were slowly replaced by the bison and the aurochs. The characteristic animal for this period was the reindeer, which was important game for the Magdalenian hunters. They not only ate its meat, but fashioned many instruments, weapons and ornamental objects from its bones and antlers.

The stone instruments of Magdalenian hunters were also found by their fires, including blades, scrapers, burins, etc. They were no longer so perfect, however, and the work shows signs of degeneration. On the other hand, an abundance of minute tools, known as microliths, made their appearance. These were fixed into wooden or bone holders, thus giving rise to composite tools. Bone instruments were more perfect than ever before. The sharp daggers, which were undoubtedly dangerous weapons, often had a hole bored in one end by which to hang them up. Harpoons, which were typical Magdalenian weapons, were made in various shapes, with one or two rows of teeth. One harpoon found in Pekárna cave in Czechoslovakia actually had three rows. Spears have also been discovered. *Batons de commandement*, whistles and flutes, which already appeared occasionally during the Aurignacian period, were now made in abundance from the bones of different animals. Small bone tools for making clothing from skins were also made in large numbers, including needles with eyes. Bone clasps are also a frequent find. The Magdalenian period also represents the culmination of Palaeolithic art.

PLATE 25

# HUNTING THE MAMMOTH

Late Palaeolithic man, who lived in larger communities than the Neanderthalers, also had considerable worry over obtaining food. Roots and berries were not enough and so he continually had to go out hunting. Improved and new weapons, new tricks and devices made hunting easier than it had been before, but it was still fatiguing and dangerous. It was not enough for the hunters to be strong; they also needed to know the habits and movements of the game and the places it frequented. It certainly required considerable ingenuity to hunt the mammoth, the wild horse, or the reindeer.

The only remaining evidence on hunting methods is provided by engravings illustrating different types of traps. It is certain, however, that the hunters went out in groups, since singly they would have had difficulty in coping with strong or swift animals.

Late Palaeolithic hunters also probably preferred to hunt young game. It seems possible that they attempted to separate young mammoths from the main herd, pursuing them and killing some of them. This is borne out by finds of the bones of young mammoths in different encampments. They also caught large animals, however, no doubt including mammoths, in camouflaged pits on frequented tracks, such as those used by game to get to the drinking pools. They even knew devices by which they could catch large numbers of animals at once.

Surprising numbers of mammoth bones have been found in some Aurignacian encampments, such as the Předmostí encampment near Přerov in Moravia (Czechoslovakia), which contained the bones of at least 1,000 mamoths from newborn young to adult specimens. The Předmostí hunters have every right to the title of 'mammoth hunters'.

The catching of a mammoth always meant a period of prosperity for the tribe. There was plenty of meat and no need to go sparingly; everyone could eat his fill — and even overeat himself if he wanted to. Those were assuredly days of rejoicing and merry-making.

PLATE 26

# HUNTING THE HAIRY RHINOCEROS

The bones found in the encampments of Late Palaeolithic hunters also include those of the hairy rhinoceros, showing that they even hunted this bad-tempered, dangerous animal. Unless they attempted to catch him by trickery, the hunt was always fraught with perils. Before he was finally killed, the rhinoceros would severely injure or kill many of his pursuers. The death of a hunter was naturally a serious loss, particularly for small tribes. This necessitated caution and avoidance of danger, but danger sometimes came suddenly and unexpectedly, with dire consequences for many a hunter.

The constant dangers involved in hunting big animals, which often resulted in severe injury, together with hardship and disease, prevented Late Palaeolithic man from living to a ripe old age. Skeletons of persons older than fifty have rarely been found. The chief diseases were rheumatism, inflammation of the joints and spine, dental decay and probably infectious diseases. Since the latter produce no pathological changes in bones, however, their existence can only be presumed.

Hunting injuries were not the only kind suffered by Late Palaeolithic man. Many of them — often fatal — were acquired from his fellows. The woman of Cro-Magnon died very young from a blow on the forehead, while a hunter in the Mladeč caves near Litovel in Moravia was killed by two blows on the back of the neck, to mention only two examples.

PLATE 27

# HUNTING THE BISON

In addition to the mammoth, the wild horses, the aurochs and the reindeer, Late Palaeolithic man also hunted the bison. This animal was hunted particularly by the Magdalenian hunters, who often depicted it. The bison gave them good, juicy meat and its hide had many uses. Magdalenian hunters appear to have set snares and traps for it. They probably separated some animals from the rest of the herd, driving them into suitable places such as rocky defiles, blind valleys and swamps, where they could be attacked and killed with less danger.

The Magdalenian hunters left many fine pictures of bisons in their engravings and paintings. Indeed, it was the paintings of bisons in the cave of Altamira which brought to light the existence of Palaeolithic art. In November 1897, eleven years after the chance discovery of Altamira by a huntsman, little Maria de Sautuola entered the cave, curious to see what her father, Marcellino de Sautuola, was looking for there. When she saw that he only raked the ground over carefully and examined it attentively, she was bored. She went cautiously into the low passage and inspected the walls and ceiling by the dim light of a candle. Suddenly she screamed: 'Toros! Toros!' ('Bulls, bulls!') and de Sautuola saw his frightened daughter running towards him away from the passage. When she told him that the ceiling was covered with pictures of 'bulls', and was not to be put off this belief, Sautuola himself crept into the passage on all fours. What he saw there astounded him. The whole ceiling was covered with magnificent paintings of bisons, with occasional pictures of other animals (deer, wild horses and wild boars). De Sautuola immediately realised that these were Palaeolithic works of art. When he submitted the report of this discovery to a congress of experts in Lisbon, in 1880, his view was rejected and refused recognition. It was many years before it was realised that de Sautuola was right and that Altamira was indeed a prehistoric picture gallery — a sort of prehistoric Louvre.

PLATE 28

# HUNTING WILD HORSES

Late Palaeolithic hunters sometimes hunted on a large scale. The best example of this is in France, near Solutré, to the north of Lyons, where wild horses were hunted.

Here there is a high, precipitous rock, at the foot of which vast quantities of bones of wild horses were discovered.

One side of this rock is 1,100 feet high, while the other slopes down to the plain. It stands like a gigantic monument over a mass grave of wild horses. At the foot of the sheer rock wall, over a tremendous area, lies a layer of bones of wild horses 18 inches to 8 feet deep. Toussaint has estimated the number of horses at 40,000; others claim that there are as many as 100,000.

This vast prehistoric Pompeii is nothing more than a relic of the large-scale hunting of Late Palaeolithic hunters, who cleverly utilised the sheer drop. They drove the horses up the gradual slope, often probably by means of fire, which the wind carried all over the hill. Frightened by the flames which blazed from the dry grass, by the smoke and by the shouts of the hunters, the horses raced up the hill to fall from the sheer precipice, where they lay with broken limbs and could be killed without difficulty.

Horses were hunted for their hides as well as for their meat.

PLATE 29

# HUNTING THE CAVE BEAR

Upper Palaeolithic hunters also hunted the cave bear. As a rule they probably lay in wait on the rocks above narrow defiles and threw boulders down on the bears. They may sometimes also have attacked them directly, in which case long spears would have been the most satisfactory weapons. The greater the number of hunters, the smaller the danger and the sooner the hunt was successful.

One relic of a fight with a cave bear proved to be particularly important. It was discovered at a time when it was still thought that man did not live at the same time as mammoths, hairy rhinoceroses and cave bears. In a cave near Sloup, not far from Boskovice in Moravia, Jindřich Wankel found the skull of a cave bear with signs of well-healed, though severe, injury to the crown. This was undoubtedly caused by the stone weapon of an Aurignacian hunter. Near the skull lay the broken point. The hunter had attacked the cave bear with a jasper-pointed spear with such force that the point was embedded in the bone and broke off. The bear survived and the wound healed, but the point of the spear remained in the skull until the animal died, in the Sloup cave. After death, when the soft tissues decayed, the broken point fell out of the bone. Wankel's finding thus refuted once and for all, all erroneous views that man had not lived at the same time as Pleistocene animals.

PLATE 30

# THE VĚSTONICE VENUS

Among the oldest works of art of Late Palaeolithic hunters are nude female figures known as 'Venuses'. The face, arms and legs are usually neglected, while the breasts, belly and thighs, i.e. the features typical for the woman-mother, are exaggerated. Many such statuettes have been found, from south Europe to as far away as Siberia. They are usually fashioned from mammoth ivory, but some are made from stone and other materials.

One such statuette was found in Dolní Věstonice on the river Dyje in Moravia. It was modelled from soft, plastic material, prepared by the artist from the ash of animal bones mixed with clay, probably kneaded together with fat, to form a beautiful female figure, which he afterwards baked in the fire until it turned as hard as stone. Perhaps it was the same artist who formed the handsome animal figures. The Věstonice Venus shows all the characteristic features of these statuettes — the great breasts, hips and thighs and the neglected face.

Another Venus found in Czechoslovakia, on Landek Hill in Ostrava-Petřkovice, was also fashioned from special material — from red iron ore. The head of this statuette is missing, however. As distinct from other Venuses the form is harmonious and not exaggerated.

All the known Venuses represent nude female figures — with one exception. This is a statuette found in Buret in the region west of Lake Baikal. The clothing is indicated schematically, but distinctly. It represents a kind of one-piece skin suit, without a front fastening and with a typical arctic hood. This clothing was very appropriate for the inclement climatic conditions of arctic regions and gave complete protection against the severe frosts and icy winds.

PLATE 31

# VENUSES

Some Venus statuettes are world renowned. One such statuette is the Venus of Willendorf in Austria (the first from the left). It represents a strong, robust, mature woman with an elaborate coiffure. It is carved from soft limestone and is 11 cm. (over 4 in.) high. Another well-known Venus is the one from Savignano in Italy (centre). This statuette is made from serpentine and is nine inches high. The Venus of Lespugue in France (on the right), carved from mammoth ivory and just under six inches high, is an artistic gem. Although displaying the usual exaggeration, the form is refined and artistically carried out. The whole figure is symmetrical, forming a regular diamond. The small head is set on a delicate, narrow chest, the body widens out into mighty hips, narrowing again towards the feet, which are only just indicated. This statuette is a product of the highest skill and aesthetic imagination.

The neglected hands and heads of these and other Venuses and the exaggeration of their feminine characteristics clearly show that later conceptions of feminine beauty and gentleness played no part in their formation. They served no erotic purpose, but were rather inspired by reverence for woman. This was the period when, as some authorities believe, matriarchism began to develop, when women occupied an important place in the economic and social sphere. With the existence of group marriages, fatherhood was unknown. Only the mother was known and relationship was therefore taken from the distaff side. The child-bearing woman was therefore an esteemed member of society. The developing tribal community thus began to derive its origin from some ancient ancestress, whom they also worshipped. These Venuses are thus probably all the object and symbol of a cult — probably a child-bearing and fertility cult.

Late Palaeolithic artists did not make small statuettes only, but sometimes painted likenesses of women on the walls of caves. One example of this work is to be found in bas-reliefs about two feet high, fashioned by Magdalenian hunters, like those discovered at Laussel in France, the most interesting of which shows a nude female figure holding a bison's horn. More in keeping with present artistic taste are the female figures recently discovered by Mlle. de St. Maturin and Dr. D. A. E. Garrod, in the Roc aux Sorciers shelter, which is also in France. In this case the Magdalenian artist carved young, slender female figures in the rock.

The table shows: the Venus of Willendorf (Austria: left), the Venus of Savignano (Italy: centre) and the Venus of Lespugue (France: right). All belong to the Aurignacian period.

3

2

1

PLATE 32

# THE PŘEDMOSTÍ VENUS

One of the longest known and most important encampments of the Aurignacian mammoth hunters in Moravia is the one at Předmostí near Přerov. It became famous long ago for finds of mammoth bones. The scholar Jan Blahoslav mentioned it 400 years ago. The splendid situation of Předmostí under the limestone rocks, with nearby moraines containing flint, the rich hunting grounds along the beds of two rivers, all combined to entice the Palaeolithic hunter to this area since the earliest ages. Several cultural layers were found in the profile of this encampment. The three middle layers, belonging to different Aurignacian stages of development, are the most important. The thickest of these is the lowest layer, which is piled with mammoth bones to a depth of over three feet. The other two layers are thin and in places are completely missing. For that period the Předmostí encampment was very large, fanning out round the eastern rock face over an area of about 2½ acres. Many stone instruments have been found there. One of the exceptional finds was a mass grave. Careful study by Professor J. Matiegka showed that some of the features of the Předmostí mammoth hunters were reminiscent of Neanderthal man, though some authorities are doubtful about this. They nevertheless belong to the race of *Homo sapiens* and probably came from the east, bringing their culture with them.

The eastern origin of the Předmostí hunters is best seen from their works of art. Many of their bone implements are decorated with simple geometric designs which quite certainly are from the east, which is the home of such ornaments. Their relationship with the east can also be seen in the Předmostí Venus, the only example of its kind in existence. It is not a sculpture, but was engraved with sharp flint burins into a fragment of mammoth tusk. The female figure is sublimated into a geometric scheme. By means of straight lines, triangles and ovals, the Aurignacian artist of Předmostí created a unique work of art fully worthy of our imagination.

PLATE 33

# STYLISED VENUSES

The body of some Venuses is schematic, so that they present over-stylised likenesses, or 'ideosculptures', which in many cases can be identified only by an expert. Such ideosculptures have been found in Czechoslovakia among relics of the Later Palaeolithic. One of these, carved from mammoth ivory and discovered in 1935 in Dolní Věstonice, appears at first sight to resemble a fork. The whole of the upper part of the body is cylindrical in form, while the legs form the whole of the lower part, with a deep groove in the middle (figure No. 4.) In 1937 another Venus was found in the same place. The upper and lower part of the body of this figure were stylised to form an ornamented cylinder, from which only the large breasts projected. A similar Venus, almost unrecognisable to the lay eye, comes from Předmostí, near Přerov. Here again the artist suppressed all details and being limited by the shape of the bone (a mammoth's sternum), he fashioned a bending female figure, probably representing a pregnant woman. These statuettes, which it is believed may have been regarded by Předmostí women as fetishes which would save them from difficult delivery, were long regarded as unique. Some years ago, however, when a large Palaeolithic settlement was discovered at Avdeyevo near Kursk, in the U.S.S.R., similar female figures made of the same material were found. There is no doubt as to their cultural kinship, but it is not known whether the people of Předmostí came to Přerov from the distant plains of Russia, or whether they moved from the west to the east.

The table shows: 1. The Venus of Malta, from the valley of the Bielaya, near the village of the same name in the region west of Lake Baikal (U.S.S.R.), a female figure lacking the marks of typical Venuses. — 2. A stylised Venus from Předmostí near Přerov, Moravia. — 3. An ideosculpture of a woman (Venus) from Dolní Věstonice on the river Dyje in Moravia. — Ideoplastic pendants resembling female figures: 4. from Dolní Věstonice. 5. from the Pekárna cave near Mokrá in the Brno district, Moravia. — 6. from Petersfels in Baden. (1 — 4: Aurignacian; 5 — 6: Magdalenian. Various sizes).

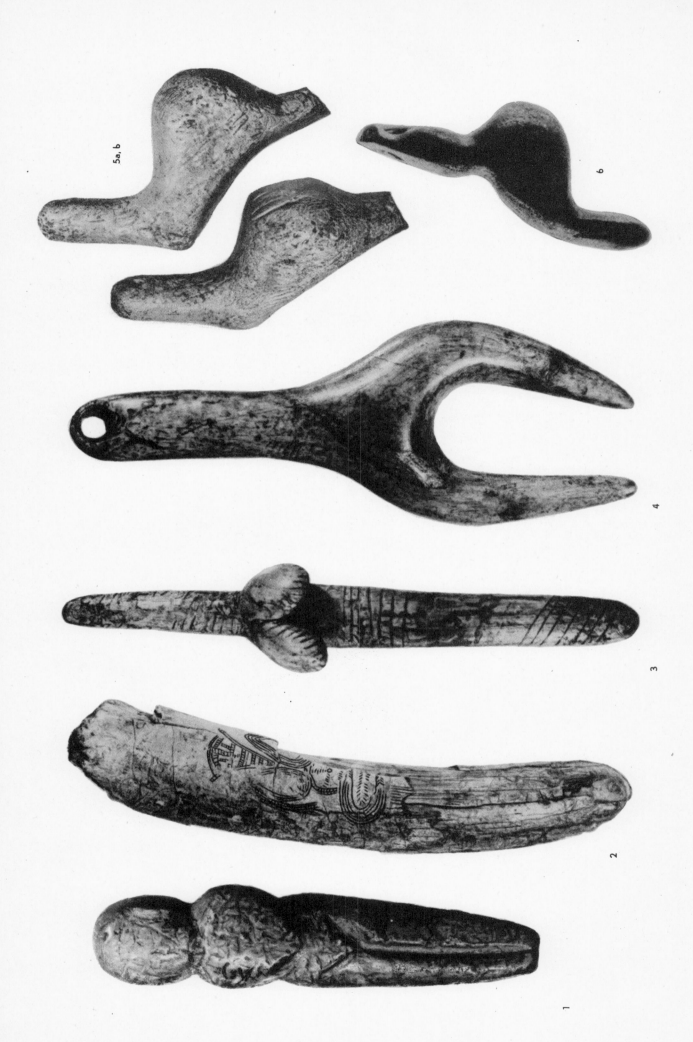

PLATE 34

# PORTRAYAL OF MAN

Late Palaeolithic man rarely portrayed his own likeness. Although the Aurignacian Venuses are anatomically well constructed, the face is always neglected or, very occasionally, indicated schematically. It is not known why the artists did not depict the face. In view of their artistic skill there is no question that they would have been able to do so. Perhaps there was some taboo associated with sorcery which forbade them. These remarks about the Venuses — which were evidently some kind of idol — also apply to the solitary nude male figure found in Brno in the grave of an Aurignacian mammoth hunter (v. figure No. 3). Engravings of human figures on bones or on the walls of caves also resemble children's efforts rather than works of art, unless they are meant to represent masked figures or caricatures (v. figure No. 2).

Occasionally, however, the human face is portrayed in sculptures and engravings, such as the human head carved in mammoth ivory, found in Dolní Věstonice. 'The piece of mammoth ivory,' wrote Academician J. Böhm, 'shows a long face with a high forehead, sloping back into the hair. The eyes gazing into infinity and the long nose with its narrow nostrils and lightly closed mouth make a face so noble in appearance that it is hard to believe that it was fashioned tens of thousands of years ago. Even the tiny cracks, partly mitigated by the yellow tone of the ancient patina, do not disturb the repose and peace of this strange face.' Alongside this head, which is one of the masterpieces of Aurignacian art, we could place two Aurignacian sculptures of human heads — one from Menton on the Riviera, the other from Brassempouy in France. Other fine figures include the Magdalenian hunter, worked in relief, discovered in the Roc aux Sorcies shelter in France and the bas-relief of a Magdalenian hunter in Laussel, also in France.

The plate shows: 1. a human head in mammoth ivory, Dolní Věstonice, Moravia. — 2. a small human figure engraved in bone, from the same place. — 3. (a-c): figure of a man in mammoth ivory (front, back and side) from Brno. All belong to the late Aurignacian (Gravettian) period.

PLATE 35

# STUDIO OF A PREHISTORIC ARTIST

The latest excavations in the mammoth hunters' encampment in Dolní Věstonice led to an interesting discovery.

The tribe possessed an artist who invented a special, soft, plastic material, which he prepared by mixing the ash of animal bones with clay, probably kneading them together with fat. No doubt he gave the problem considerable thought before he invented this excellent modelling material which, when baked in the fire, hardened like a stone and kept its form forever. It was from this material that the famous Venus of Věstonice and many handsome animal figures were made.

This was not the prehistoric artist's only invention, however. He made an even more important discovery. A small hut, about 16 feet long and 13 feet wide, was found in the encampment, at some little distance from the other huts, on a gentle slope near a small brook. In the middle of this hut a hollow had been made for the fire. This was lined with clay and had a vault, like a primitive kiln, such as those found in the dwellings of the earliest Neolithic farmers. Lumps of modelling material, half formed figures and the baked heads of a bear and fox lay round the kiln. This shows that an ordinary fire was not adequate for baking the statuettes of the Věstonice artist, but that he had built a kiln for the purpose. This is an absolutely unique discovery which shows that the artist of the Věstonice mammoth hunters of the late Aurignacian (Gravettian) period not only invented a new plastic material, but that he was also the first to discover and create ceramics. Neolithic man thus only invented a new *form* of ceramics — pottery.

It would be interesting to know why the Věstonice artist had to leave his workshop in such haste, why he had to interrupt what he was doing, leaving everything in disorder. It would also be interesting to know if he lived (or at least worked) in the hut himself, somewhat apart from the life of the encampment. Perhaps he needed peace and solitude for his work, to escape from the curiosity of the rest of the tribe. Since it can be assumed that his works of art were chiefly the trappings of hunting, sorcery or of some other cult, his solitude would no doubt be respected by the others and he would be regarded as an esteemed, though somewhat mysterious, person. It is not known whether the artist was also the sorcerer of the tribe (v. Tab. 47 and the appended text), but it is possible that some of the figures were made directly for the sorcerer.

One other remarkable find from the same place may be a direct relic of the artist himself. The first finger print on record was found on the figure of the bear; other prints of fingers and palms were found on lumps of the plastic substance. They show that the pattern of the whorls did not differ from the finger prints of modern man.

PLATE 36

# ANIMAL FIGURES

Late Palaeolithic artists did not model nude female figures and occasional nude male figures only. Beautiful animal figures have also been found in their encampments in different countries.

Some figures have been found in Czechoslovakia. In the mammoth hunters' encampment in Předmostí, near Přerov, a splendid figure of a mammoth, carved from mammoth ivory, was found (figure No. 1). Many animal figures, made from the special plastic material described above, were found in the mammoth hunters' encampment in Dolní Věstonice, including figures of the cave bear, the wild horse, the hairy rhinoceros, the mammoth, the wolverine, the reindeer, the arctic owl and other creatures (figures No. 2 and No. 3). One of these prehistoric animal sculptures is particularly interesting. It is a stylised reindeer head, expressed in geometric grouping of deeply carved lines running in a transverse direction on the top of the head and longitudinally along the sides. The eyes, ears and forehead are marked by raised ridges. The style in which this head is carried out is clearly influenced by the eastern (Ukrainian) centre of Aurignacian art, which influenced Věstonice artists more strongly than the western (French) centre.

Animal figures have also been found elsewhere, many of them beautifully carried out, showing the animal in a given posture or motion. A magnificent figure of a wild horse was found in Lourdes in France. In Mas d'Azil — also in France — the head of a neighing horse was found, admirably carved from a reindeer horn, while from Bruniquel in France come engravings of running reindeer in mammoth ivory.

Arrows are carved on the bodies of many of these figures, clearly showing that they were primarily part of some hunting magic cult.

The plate shows: 1. Figure of a mammoth in mammoth ivory from Předmostí, near Přerov, Moravia. — 2. and 3. Figures of a mammoth and cave bear from ceramic material found in Dolní Věstonice, Moravia.
All belong to the Late Aurignacian (Gravettian) period.

PLATE 37

# BONE ARTICLES I

The Aurignacian mammoth hunters knew how to select the sites for their encampments. If they set them up in the open, they always chose a sunny southern slope, protected, if possible, from the north winds by overhanging rocks or by mountains. They always camped near water, but not so close as to be in danger from floods. The view also played an important part in selection of the site, since it was necessary to follow the movements of animals or of hostile tribes. The main requirement, however, was that there should be an abundant supply of game.

Game was not hunted for meat only, but also for skins, which the hunters wore as clothing, or used to cover their tent-like dwellings, and on which they lay down to sleep. The bones were thrown into ditches dug specially for waste; some, however, were carefully put aside to be made into implements, weapons and useful or ornamental articles. This stock of 'raw materials' was often neatly arranged, such as the store in Předmostí, where 13 mammoth tusks, 50 mammoth molars and 13 wolf skulls were all stacked tidily together.

Some bone, horn or ivory articles were fashioned in a truly masterly manner and were sometimes decorated with tasteful ornaments or animal engravings.

The table shows: 1. a fork-like object. — 2. a spade-like object with ornament. — 3. needles with eyes. — 4. a and b: instrument for smoothing (front and side view). — 5. 'bâton de commandement' (not decorated). — 6. dagger made from lion's bone, — 7 and 8. clasps. All belong to the later Aurignacian (Gravettian) period and come from Předmostí, near Přerov, Moravia.

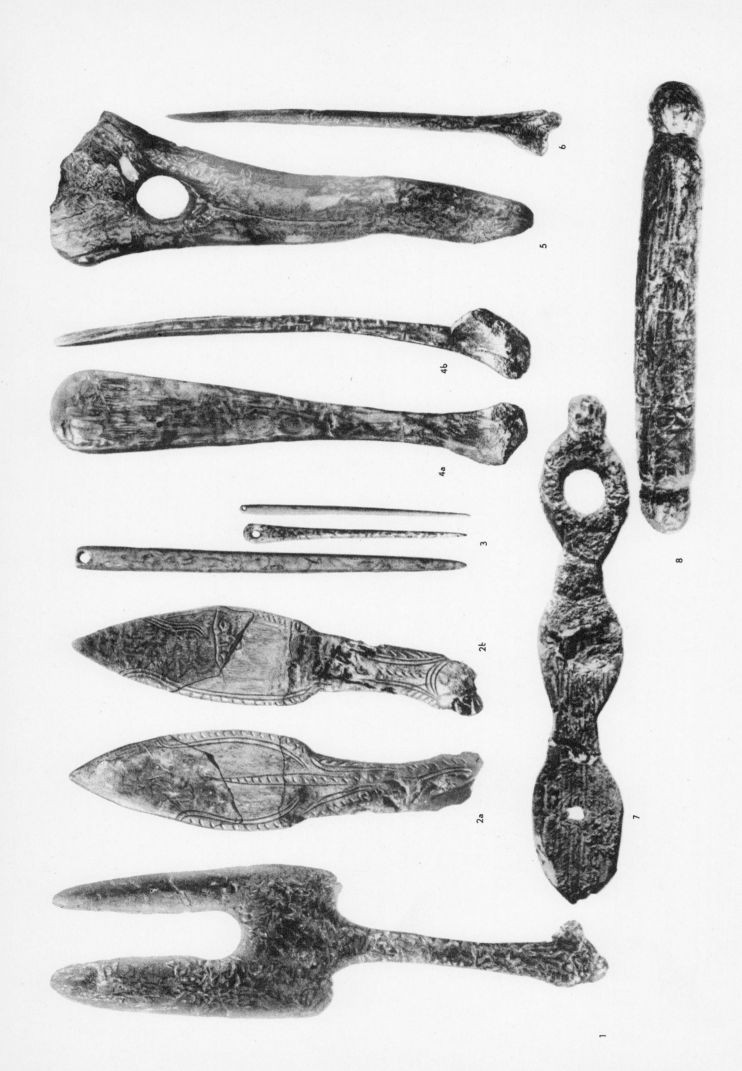

PLATE 38

# BONE ARTICLES II

Magdalenian hunters were very fond of making weapons, implements and other useful objects from bone and horn. Many of these were more perfect versions of earlier weapons, others were newly invented.

Characteristic of these hunters is the 'bâton de commandement', a peculiar bone object with a hole bored in one end and sometimes beautifully decorated with engravings. It is impossible to say whether they actually were a sign of leadership; they might equally well have belonged to the sorcerer or have been used in magic rites. There are several alternative explanations. Whistles and flutes are often found among the work of Magdalenian hunters, although whistles were already occasionally used by Later Aurignacian hunters, such as those of Věstonice. The whistles were made from the bones of different creatures, but mainly bones of birds and reindeer. The arsenal of Magdalenian hunters boasted new weapons, including bone points with a groove for letting blood so that the animal died sooner by loss of blood, and harpoons, usually armed with two rows of teeth. Another important invention was a special stick for hurling spears with greater velocity and penetrating force. The spear points were made of bone.

The table shows several bone products made by Magdalenian hunters found in the Pekárna cave near Mokrá in the Brno district, Moravia.

1. 'bâton de commandement', undecorated. — 2. 'bâton de commandement', decorated with animal engravings. — 3. whistles from reindeer toe joints. — 4. bowl made from reindeer's skull. — 5. points and needles. — 6. bone articles with cleft (front and side views) — harpoon (back and front view).

PLATE 39

# MAKING NECKLACES

Man's desire to adorn himself is as old as the hills. In some encampments of Later Palaeolithic hunters, as in Věstonice, large quantities of lumps of coloured clay have been found strewn about. They probably served for painting the body, since this is the oldest form of adornment known and Late Palaeolithic hunters certainly painted themselves on festive occasions or for magic rites.

Other forms of adornment are also found among Aurignacian hunters, however, including necklaces, usually made from the shells of molluscs and snails, from the teeth of wild animals or from beads cut from mammoth's tusks. All the parts of the necklace, whether from shells or teeth, always have a hole by which they can be threaded. Some necklaces are made of the same type of parts, such as shells of one type; sometimes they are made from different objects, such as shells and teeth. In Mainz, in Germany, a whole Aurignacian workshop was found for the production of such necklaces. Around flat-topped stones, which were probably used as tables, among quantities of flint instruments, lay numbers of shells of Tertiary marine molluscs of the genus *Cerithium*, from which many of the points had been broken off.

Not all necklaces were meant merely for adornment. Many were probably worn as amulets, to protect the wearer from danger, accident and disease. Some were probably connected with some cult, like the one just being completed by the hunter in this picture. The finding of the schematic Venus from the same place (Dolní Věstonice, Table 34, figure No. 3), strongly suggests that the whole of this necklace is actually composed of beads representing the breasts of this figure. When it is known that Venuses were the objects of a motherhood-fertility cult, it seems probable that this necklace was probably a magic talisman for ensuring fertility and growth of the tribe, since there was always a need for more healthy children. This explains the interest in fertility of the women, which had to be aided by magic talismans and amulets.

PLATE 40

# NECKLACES

The necklaces of Late Palaeolithic hunters were not always made of one type of material, such as shells of the same species of snails of different sizes. A necklace found in Hundsteig in Austria was made of shells of recent and extinct snails from quite different places. It included the present-day species *Cyclonassa neritea*, while of extinct species the artist used shells of *Melanopsis vindobonensis* from the Pliocene rocks in the area of Lake Balaton in Hungary and conches of the species *Lithoglyphus naticoides* from Hungarian Pleistocene layers. A particularly interesting necklace was found at Arcy-sur-Cure in France. Alongside a quantity of small shells with holes in them, Ficatier found a trilobite in which two holes had been drilled so that it could be worn as a pendant, or probably as a strange and potent talisman. The nearest place in France where trilobites are found is at some distance, in Brittany and Normandy. Douvillé, however, was of the opinion that this trilobite did not come from France at all, but from Czechoslovakia. Both these necklaces (and others) indicate that Late Palaeolithic hunter-artists noticed these fossils on their travels, collected suitable specimens and used them in the making of necklaces. It is even possible that exchanges were made with other tribes. Some necklaces were made of a small number of parts, others of a large number, such as the necklace found in the grave of an Aurignacian hunter in Brno, which was made of 600 tusk shells of the extinct species *Dentalium badense*.

Impressive necklaces were made from the canine teeth of beasts of prey, particularly if they were mixed. One unique specimen composed of 42 fox canines, arranged criss-cross, was found in Dolní Věstonice.

The plate shows: 1. a necklace of ornamented cylindrical beads of mammoth ivory. — 2. a necklace of gastropod shells of the genus *Cerithium*. — 3. a necklace of bear and wolf canines. — 4. a necklace of wolf and fox canines. —
All belong to the later Aurignacian (Gravettian) period and come from Dolní Věstonice, South Moravia.

PLATE 41

# ENGRAVINGS

Animal engravings are often encountered in Late Palaeolithic art.

This is not surprising, since Palaeolithic man was first and foremost a hunter and the welfare of the tribe depended on the success of the hunt. Game is therefore portrayed the most frequently, particularly the mammoth, reindeer, wild horse, aurochs and bison, less frequently the wild boar, ibex, the cave bear and the brown bear, and only occasionally the hairy rhinoceros, chamois, arctic hare and other animals. Pictures of beasts of prey are rare on the whole (with occasional engravings of the cave lion, the wolf, the wolverine, the otter and the arctic fox); the same applies to birds, reptiles and fish. Engravings of plants are rarest of all.

Large numbers of animal engravings are known. All show that the artist was well acquainted with the game which he portrayed on ivory, horn, bone, stone, stalactites and stalagmites and the walls of caves. Many animals are vividly depicted in a typical posture or in motion and sometimes they are engraved so perfectly that different species can be distinguished (e.g. species of wild horses). Among the rare engravings of dying animals is one of a reindeer engraved in stone in Gourdan in France and the beautiful engraving from the Trois Frères cave in France, showing a young brown bear killed by arrows, with blood spouting from its jaws.

Not all engravings are successful or of the same artistic value. Many must be regarded as mere sketches or as the work of amateurs, lacking the sensitive hand, the observant eye — and the talent. Often so many animals are carved, one on top of the other, higgledy-piggledy, on flat stone, that they make a picture-puzzle. This is also found, on a larger scale, in caves, where some of the walls are covered with innumerable engravings, looking at first glance like a chaotic scrawl, which require considerable experience, knowledge and time to decipher.

The only tools of these prehistoric artists were flint burins. Despite the simplicity of their instruments, however, some of their works of art are truly admirable and of high artistic value, particularly when the artist ingeniously utilised the uneven surface of the rocky foundation to simulate mass in engravings on cave walls.

The plate shows engravings of animals in the caves of Font-de-Gaumes and Les Combarelles in France, an engraving of a stag in the cave of Altamira in Spain, engravings of wild horses from Les Combarelles, the engraving of the killing of a brown bear in the Trois Frères cave in France and the engraving of a male and female aurochs in Grotte de la Mairie (Reyaut), also in France (from Breuil, Capitan and Peyron).

PLATE 42

# ENGRAVINGS ON BONE

Late Palaeolithic hunter-artists also engraved pictures in bone, from simple carvings, such as those found on fragments of mammoth bones in the settlement of Avdeyevo near Kursk in the U.S.S.R. and elsewhere, to splendid geometric ornaments (like the bracelet from Mizin in the U.S.S.R.) and magnificent animal engravings sometimes in typical postures (such as the picture of a charging mammoth on a fragment of mammoth tusk from La Madeleine in France, or of a grazing reindeer on a fragment of reindeer antler in the Kesslerloch in Switzerland, etc.). In some engravings distant animals are shown on a smaller scale (such as the bone with engravings of horses' heads from Isturitz in France); others show herds of animals, such as the impressionist engraving on an eagle's bone showing a herd of reindeer crossing the tundra, which was found at Teyjat in France. One rare specimen, showing a duel between bisons, engraved on a horse's rib, was found in Pekárna cave near Mokrá, in the Brno district, Czechoslovakia. The two bisons are charging one another, heads down, while a third, with arrows engraved on its body, is galloping towards them.

Engravings on bones, like engravings on stones, did not develop from the artist's desire to express his own experiences. The main motive behind these engravings is hunting magic. The great advantage of these small engravings on bones and stones as compared with engravings (and paintings) on the walls of caves was that they were always to hand, whenever needed for the magic rites and sorcery which the hunter was convinced would help him to overcome life's difficulties.

The plate shows engravings on bone from the Pekárna cave near Mokrá: 1. engraving of an animal's head on a fragment of reindeer antler. — 2. simple rows of carving on a bone. — 3. engraving of a duel between two bisons engraved on a horse's rib. — 4. spatula-like object with animal engravings.

Different sizes, all belonging to the Magdalenian period.

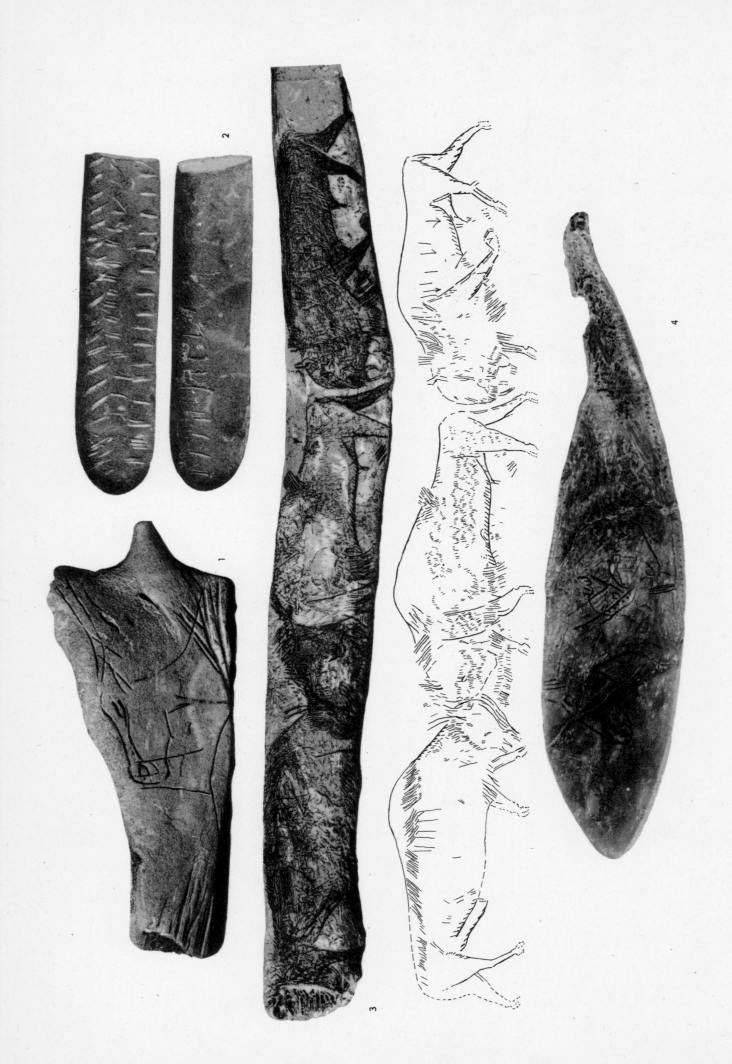

PLATE 43

# IN AN UNDERGROUND PICTURE GALLERY

The magnificent coloured paintings which adorn the walls of some French and Spanish caves belong to the most remarkable and most valuable relics of Palaeolithic art, the oldest art in the world. Some of these paintings are truly great works of art and some caves are veritable prehistoric picture galleries. Four of the finest are the Altamira cave in Spain and the Font-de-Gaume, Niaux and Lascaux caves in France.

The Late Palaeolithic artist (mainly during the Magdalenian period) worked under great difficulties. With no other light than the dim flicker of stone lamps or the blaze of pine torches he often painted high, almost inaccessible cave walls, or, bending and lying on his back, he painted the ceilings of the low passages. His colours were all of mineral origin, being coloured earths, specimens of which have been preserved in some caves until today. They are found in lumps of different sizes, weighing up to several pounds. Sometimes the lumps have broken up into coloured dust. Occasionally these colours are found in the form of pointed crayons — the oldest in existence. Before the artist started to paint, he crushed the lumps of clay, obtaining a fine dust which he mixed with animal fat. An animal's shoulder-blade or a flat stone would serve as a palette. Whether he painted with his finger, with twigs or with some kind of brush made from animal hair or feathers we do not know.

The paintings in the caves may have been the work of many generations and of different tribes, whose most gifted members executed the finest of these pictures. It has even been suggested that there were already 'schools' of art, which produced pupils who not only mastered the technique of painting, but also took over given traditions which they followed in the choice of content of their own paintings.

Mention should be made of one particularly interesting question. Evidence from a number of sources shows that mural paintings were also done on a small scale, i.e. that they were also engraved in stone or bone. Were these the sketches for a projected mural, or were they copies of existing paintings? It is difficult to say which, especially as there are cases in which the miniature was found far from the site of the actual painting, such as the engraving of a bison found 220 miles away from the Font-de-Gaume cave which contains a faithful mural replica of this engraving.

The number of paintings in different caves varies, sometimes reaching several hundreds. Their dimensions also vary. For example, in the Lascaux cave is the picture of an aurochs 67 inches long, in black (shown here), below which the prehistoric artist has painted tiny horses.

PLATE 44

# PICTURES FEATURING ARROWS

The Late Palaeolithic artist did not paint or engrave his pictures simply to satisfy his own love of beauty. The animals were depicted as the object of the hunt, as something of which the artist wanted to gain possession. The welfare of the tribe was completely dependent on the fortunes of the hunt and it was important that everything should be done to ensure success. 'The first people,' wrote Jiří Neústupný, 'sought help everywhere where they thought they might find it. Their first care was how to ensure that the hunt would be successful, since on this their very life frequently depended. The primitive way of thinking of the first people led them directly to the idea of hunting magic. This was undoubtedly the main, if not the only, thing which stimulated the development of their art. The hunters believed that depiction of a wounded or trapped animal would result at the earliest opportunity in the wounding or trapping of a real animal. The hunt, or battle with the enemy, would take place exactly as shown in the magic picture. They simply gave concrete form to the desired effect, to their own wishes, thus increasing the magic power for the first time. With their direct religious outlook they did not simply see the picture of an animal; they saw the animal itself. The picture and the reality were one and the same thing to them. This explains why the first art is so naturalistic, why it does not begin with simple forms and signs of a symbolic character. The pictures are clearly true to life because in that case the spell would be more effective. It was thus in the interests of the whole tribe that the artist should produce a picture as close as possible to reality.' This view, that prehistoric art was primarily a part of hunting sorcery, is now almost generally accepted.

The Late Palaeolithic artist, therefore, did not paint animals simply from the desire to create a work of art, or from the need to express his own experiences and impressions. He drew them as game, as something to be caught. That is why he also painted traps in front of them or on them, why he painted arrows and darts in their bodies, as in this picture of a bison in the cave of Niaux. Some pictures even show that actual arrows were used. These pictures are not pictures in our sense; they are themselves the object depicted. The drawing of an animal struck by a real or painted arrow or dart was a guarantee that the animal would actually be killed in that way. If something went wrong it was not the fault of the magic picture, but because the preparations were not properly carried out. Traces of this outlook are also encountered in more highly developed cultures and we even find it today, in the world of superstition.

PLATE 45

# PICTURES OF SORCERERS

If sorcery existed, there must also have been magicians. Their portraits are also found in prehistoric art. They are all pictures of human beings in animal masks.

It is likely that sorcerers used different objects for their magic rites, many of which they made themselves, such as rattles made from dried bladders, amulets and ornaments for wearing in the hair. They may also have been able to make primitive whistles, flutes and drums. Their 'props' may also have included the batons which were occasionally found among Aurignacian relics and were commoner in the Magdalenian period. One such baton was found in August 1908 by Bourrinet, in an abri near Mège. It was made from part of a deer's antler. The rough surface had been carefully scraped smooth and polished and a hole had been made at both ends. In addition to the engraving of a wild horse, the head of a roe-deer, three swans and three snakes, are three masked human figures dancing or leaping.

The most impressive picture of a sorcerer is the one discovered in the Trois Frères cave near Montesquieu-Avantès in South France. It dominates the pictures of animals which cover the whole wall of the cave. The sorcerer is shown stepping forward; he has a horse's tail and is clad in the skin of some beast of prey (a bear or a lion); his head is crowned with a stag's antlers, he has long ears and two large, round, piercing eyes look out from his face, which is covered with a long, pointed beard (top picture). Another picture of a sorcerer was found in the same cave. This one is enveloped in a bison's skin; he is playing a flute and dancing (bottom right).

In addition to drawings of sorcerers and masked people, drawings of creatures half-human, half animal have also been found. In Altamira, Cartailhac and Breuil found human figures with animals' heads produced into strange beaks. Other similar monsters were found in the Trois Frères cave (a bison with human legs, bottom left), in the Les Combarelles cave and elsewhere. All the pictures are from Breuil.

PLATE 46

# MAGIC RITES

The hunters gathered round the small fire, ready to set out hunting. There was no talking, but all looked tensely at the approaching sorcerer. He had a bear-skin thrown over his shoulder and round his neck was a necklace of cave-bear teeth. His face was painted and his long hair, glistening with grease, was twisted into a knot. Red spots, ringed with short lines, glowed on his hairy chest. In his hand he held a number of small animal figures kneaded from clay and ash, only partly hardened.

Stopping in front of the fire he threw a few dry branches on to the embers and when they blazed up he began to leap round the fire, waving his arms and twisting his body in a weird manner. The hunters watched, fascinated. When the sorcerer suddenly stopped, opened his hand and took out one small animal figure after another they were amazed. They had never seen anything like it before; it must be some new kind of magic. They were even more astounded when the sorcerer declaimed: 'Death to all the animals which ye hunt! May they fall into your traps, may they go lame, may their bodies be pierced with your arrows and darts!' With each new curse, the sorcerer broke off the head and legs of a figure, scattering them round him and throwing the trunk into the fire. When the last piece had finally been thrown away, he again began to leap round the fire. Suddenly he gave a wild screech, threw out his arms and shouted: 'Now set forth to the hunt! With my powerful magic to aid you, the prize will be rich!'

Some such magic rites may once have been performed in the mammoth hunters' encampment in Věstonice. It can be assumed that this was the case, as large numbers of 'mutilated' animal figures were found there — bodies without heads and legs, heads and legs without bodies. Professor K. Absolon, who discovered them, was immediately struck by this circumstance and was the first to interpret the mutilation of the figures as part of some hunting magic ceremony. This may well be the true explanation, especially when we recall the superstition, still in existence today, that if a figure representing a particular person is destroyed, that person will die immediately or very shortly.

PLATE 47

# THE TEMPLE OF THE BEAR

If the many caves richly decorated with engravings and paintings can be regarded as a kind of prehistoric temple, this is doubly true of caves in which animal statues have been preserved, such as the Tuc d'Audobert cave in South France, in which, in 1912, Count Begouen and his three sons discovered in the last cavern of an underground network of caves, the statue of two bisons modelled in the damp clay of the cave, surrounded by the marks of the feet of dancing young people. This ancient temple was no doubt the scene of magic rites associated with fertility of man and beasts. Another prehistoric temple, discovered in 1923 by Norbert Casteret in the cave of Montespan, also in South France, was the scene of a hunting magic cult.

The bear temple can be entered only by way of the river bed. After passing through a number of passages we reach a small space in which stands the roughly modelled statue of a headless bear. This statue, which is about 24 inches high, never possessed a head. Before the rites started, however, a real bear's head was placed on its shoulders. This is attested by the finding of a bear's skull in the earth in front of the statue's forepaws. It is even possible that the statue was covered with a bear-skin.

When the statue was ready, the hunters — no doubt led by the sorcerer — performed a dance round it, shooting arrows or throwing darts. Traces of arrow or spear points can still be seen on the statue.

Prehistoric temples (whether with statues or only with paintings) are usually found in almost inaccessible, remote and concealed places, as if to guard them from the curiosity of the uninitiated.

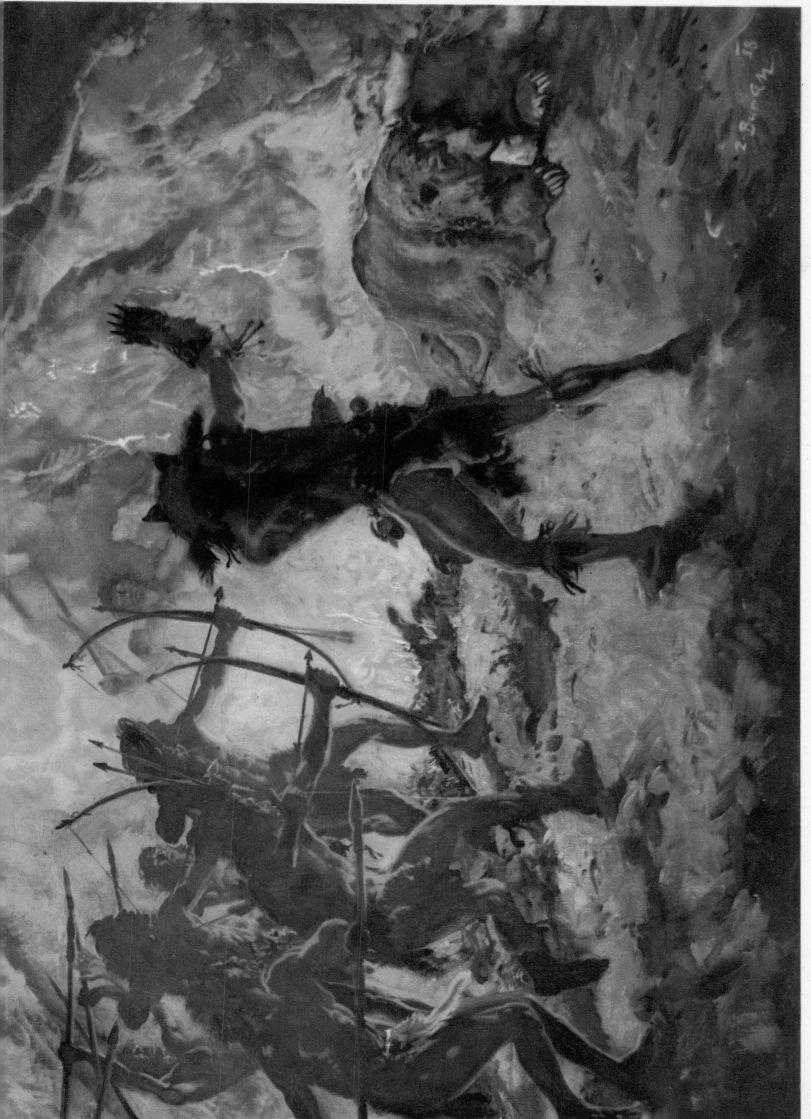

PLATE 48

# MAMMOTH HUNTER'S GRAVE

The hard life, frequent wounding when hunting or fighting enemies, together with different diseases, caused a high death rate among Aurignacian and Magdalenian hunters. There are many examples, particularly during the Aurignacian period, of ceremonial burials. A few are mentioned here.

In 1891, in the middle of Brno, the capital of Moravia, sewage workers found the grave of an Aurignacian mammoth hunter at a depth of 15 feet. He may have been a prominent member of the tribe, who was held in special esteem, since he had been accorded an elaborate burial. The shallow grave was lined with soft furs, and the dead hunter, carefully dressed in furs decorated with bone discs, was laid to rest. His neck was encircled by a long, elaborate necklace of tusk shells; stone implements and weapons lay to hand and even food appears not to have been forgotten. Finally, in accordance with the common practice of that period, his fellows sprinkled the body with red ochre and covered it with a mammoth's shoulder blade supported by a mammoth's tusk. On completing all the rites — the nature of which is not known, but the existence of which cannot be doubted — they covered the grave with earth and moved to a different place.

The Brno grave is famous because the last gifts to the dead man on his journey into eternity included the nude male figure carved from mammoth ivory. This figure is a unique find. The nude female figures known as Venuses are found from South Europe to Siberia, but male statuettes are few and far between. It is not known precisely why this was so, but it is probably associated with the fact that among Late Palaeolithic hunters the conception of fertility was always connected with woman, never with man.

Many thousands of years passed over the grave of this Late Palaeolithic hunter. When he was found, all that was left of him was his bones, surrounded by bone and stone gifts. They tell us plainly, however, that once, long ago, lived a mighty hunter who killed many mammoths and was held in great esteem by his tribe.

PLATE 49

# WOMAN'S GRAVE IN VĚSTONICE

The existence of the mammoth hunters' encampment in Dolní Věstonice, South Moravia, has been known for a long time. The first written mention of it, in 1659, by a Brno physicist, Johannes Hertold, a native of nearby Mikulov, describes the finding of a large bone which had been dug out of the ground. Hertold naturally did not know that it was a mammoth's bone. In those days such bones were thought to be the bones of giants. Although thorough and well-directed research begun in 1924 by Professor Karel Absolon brought to light many rare and remarkable relics of the life and culture of the Věstonice mammoth hunters, nothing was found of the hunters themselves apart from two incomplete crania, a few fragments of bone and fragments of a child's skeleton. In July, 1949, however, a remarkable find was made.

In the summer of that year, workers engaged in uncovering two mammoth shoulder blades, came across red-coloured earth, showing that they were over the grave of a member of the Věstonice tribe of mammoth hunters. This was found to be actually the case. In a shallow hollow lay a half-decayed female skeleton, with the legs drawn up.

Many thousands of years had elapsed since the Věstonice mammoth hunters had placed the dead woman, no doubt wrapped in furs, in her shallow grave. They laid her on her side, after first strapping her into a bundle, for fear that she might rise again from the dead and interfere in the lives of the living. Into her hand they pressed ten teeth of an arctic fox. Under her chin they placed a flint point and between her legs a sharp flint knife. They also gave her meat, of which only a few bones remained. They then sprinkled the body with red ochre and covered it with two mammoth shoulder-blades, one of which was marked with mysterious engravings which may have been related to the burial rites.

This grave of a small, dainty woman about forty years old, belonging to the tribe of the Věstonice mammoth hunters, was found at no great depth below an old cart track, which had cut deeper and deeper into the soft dusty ground. In a little while the wheels of the heavily laden carts might have destroyed it altogether.

PLATE 50

# THE CHILDREN'S GRAVE IN MENTON

Late Palaeolithic hunters buried their children as well as their adults. One of the most famous children's graves was discovered in Menton in a small cave named the Grotte des Enfants (the Children's Grotto) after this find. The cave contained two children, laid close to one another, so that it looks as if they died at the same time. The elder was about ten years old. Both lay on their backs, with their arms beside their bodies. When the skeletons were discovered, the pelvises were covered with some thousand small snail shells of the genus *Nassa*, which had probably been sewn in their clothing as ornaments.

This little cave is altogether interesting. Graves of adults were also found there. A little below the children's grave lay the grave of a woman with unusually delicate bones. Below this grave was yet another, in which a man was buried. The man lay on his back and his head and legs were protected by large stone slabs supported by stones. Below this was a further grave, which was particularily interesting. Directly on the site of the fire lay the skeleton of a young man on its right side, with the legs drawn up so that the heels almost touched the spine. Later, an old woman had been buried beside him, this time with the legs drawn up until the knees almost touched the chin. On the skull of the young man lay four rows of snail shells of the genus *Nassa* in which holes had been drilled — evidently decorating his headdress. The woman wore a shell bracelet on her left arm. A few flint instruments had been placed in the grave as gifts. The heads of both bodies were protected by a stone slab supported by two big stones. All the graves belong to the Aurignacian period.

The Grotte des Enfants belongs to the Grimaldi group of caves near Menton on the Riviera. The others also contained important graves. In the nearby Grotte du Cavillon lay the grave of a young man, sprinkled with red ochre. Near the skeleton lay a bone dagger and flint tools, while the skull was surrounded by shells of the genus *Nassa* and deer's teeth, which probably decorated the headdress. The Barma-Grande cave contained several graves. In one was a male skeleton whose skull had been sprinkled with red ochre, while another was a triple grave containing man, woman and child and in a third grave the skeleton lay with the legs drawn up, directly on the site of the fire. These graves also belonged to the Aurignacian period.

PLATE 51

# A NEOLITHIC SETTLEMENT

The Palaeolithic and the Mesolithic came to an end.

About 3,000 years B. C. the first farmers settled in Central Europe and along the whole of the Danube valley. Using primitive methods and primitive implements (hooked branches, stone and antler hoes) they tilled small fields in which they grew wheat, barley, millet and some leguminous plants. They reaped the grain with stone sickles and knives. They ground it on big stones into coarse flour. Pulpy farinaceous food, sweetened and mixed with fat, was an important addition to the diet, which had previously consisted mainly of meat. These people who lived at the beginning of the Neolithic were not only the first farmers. They also learned how to domesticate certain animals and produced pottery, which they decorated with scrolls (voluted ceramics, the oldest stage of neolithic culture) and later with *chevrons*.

Tilling the soil, the breeding of domestic animals, improved methods of making stone implements (by grinding and drilling), the production of pottery and textiles, all are unmistakable evidence of the higher standard of living of the first farmers, whose general development progressed with increasing rapidity right from the outset of the Neolithic. The countryside acquired a new appearance. Farmers built more durable dwellings, which they grouped in settlements. This gave rise to the first villages and by dint of hard, intelligent labour man began visibly to change the face of nature. A region settled by the oldest farmers remained settled and thus became not only the foundation of further cultural and economic development down to historic times, but also formed a basis for new social laws. Only when these are known and taken into account is it likely that the development of mankind can be correctly explained.

PLATE 52

*The authors wish to thank the State Pedagogical Publishing House in Prague for making available to them a number of the originals which are reproduced in this book. Plates 2, 8, 18, 23, 26, 29 and 52 were painted in collaboration with the Academician Jan Filip, Plate 23 also in collaboration with Dr Jiří Malý. Some of the plates are taken from earlier books by Professor Josef Augusta, while others were painted specially for this volume. The authors' thanks are also due to Dr Karel Žebera, who lent them the photographs for Plate 41. The material depicted in the plates comes from excavation sites in Moravia and forms part of the collections of the Moravian Museum in Brno.*